Amateur Radio Exam Secrets

2nd Edition

*Revision and practice questions covering
all three UK amateur radio examinations*

Alan Betts, G0HIQ

Radio Society of Great Britain

Published by the Radio Society of Great Britain,
3 Abbey Court, Fraser Road, Priory Business Park, Bedford MK44 3WH, UK

First published 2009

Reprinted five times 2010 - 2016

This edition printed 2017

ISBN: 9781 9050 8648 1

Publisher's note
The opinions expressed in this book are those of the author and not necessarily those of the RSGB. While the information presented is believed to be correct, the author, the publisher and their agents cannot accept responsibility for consequences arising from any inaccuracies or omissions.

Cover design: Kim Meyern
Sub-editing, layout and design: Steve Telenius-Lowe, 9M6DXX
Production & Revisions: Mark Allgar, M1MPA

Printed in Great Britain by CPI Anthony Rowe of Chippenham, Wiltshire

**Updates to this book may be found on the RSGB website
at www.rsgb.org/booksextra**

Contents

Introduction

This book is intended to be a companion for those who have started their studies and would like a quick reference and some sample examination questions. It does not seek to cover every aspect and starting from scratch is best done with the three course books (*Foundation Licence Now!*, the *Intermediate Licence Book*, and *Advance! The Full Licence Manual*) and one of the many training courses run mostly by local clubs.

This guide and the sample questions are divided into the topic areas in the Syllabus for the exams. Each section is numbered as in the syllabus and has a brief introduction to the material, followed by a number of sample questions. The correct answers are at the back of the book. This is repeated for each level: Foundation, Intermediate and Advanced. Where a topic has been adequately covered at a lower level, it is not repeated, even if the syllabus shows it is examinable at the higher level: the introductory words to the syllabus advise that it will be assumed that material in lower examinations will be known background material. Questions will be on the appropriate syllabus topic but may require knowledge of other areas to enable a sensible interpretation of the question.

Sample papers for the Foundation, Intermediate and Advanced examinations complete this book and the correct answers are provided.

Reference material is provided for each examination and is included at the back of the book.

The examinations' question banks are not published and are not available for general use. This is because the aim of the training courses and examinations is to test the candidate's understanding of the material, rather than their ability to remember facts. The questions in this book are typical of those you will meet in the exams, but they are not the actual questions.

Of course at Foundation level remembering the basics is important. At Intermediate there are more questions requiring understanding, while at Advanced level most of the questions are looking for an understanding of the subject. Don't let that put you off. The three training books are designed to be straightforward to read and to prepare you for the exam. It will be much better and certainly much more fun if you also attend a training course. The majority do, but it is not compulsory.

The Specification

The 'Specification' is a formal document (including a Syllabus) explaining the reasons for the examination and how the material you have covered will be assessed. The syllabus shows what is examined. It is fairly detailed and may not be the first thing you want to read. Nonetheless, as you progress through your studies you may like to read it and are encouraged to do so. The Specification is available to read and print off on the Radio Communications Foundation (RCF) website and there are links from the Radio Society of Great Britain (RSGB) website:

RCF: www.commsfoundation.org/rce
RSGB: www.rsgb.org.uk/tutors

Note: The Specification and reference material are updated from time to time and items such as the Band Plan are updated by the International Amateur Radio Union (IARU) to a separate timescale. A new Specification will be published at least six months before it is in use for examinations and both the publication date and in-use date are shown on the front cover. Changes to Band Plans are unlikely to require a syllabus change but the overall document, the Specification, is updated, again to show the new reference material and the date from which it will be used in the examination.

If there are any changes that affect this book, updates may be found on the RSGB website at:
http://www.rsgb.org/books/extra/examsecrets.htm

Licence scheme format
Foundation
The training course lasts typically for 12 hours, perhaps over two days or a few evenings, during which the theory and practical aspects are covered. There is a practical assessment of on-air operating using HF and VHF / UHF transceivers and setting up a station. The exam consists of 25 multiple choice questions with four possible answers and lasts 55 minutes. You need to identify the correct answer for at least 18 of them, so the pass mark is 72%.

Intermediate
The course will be around 20 hours and the practical element consists of soldering and a construction project. The exam comprises 45 questions and one hour twenty five minutes is allowed. The pass mark is 27 correct answers, or 60%.

Advanced
The training course is rather longer, perhaps 30 to 36 hours and there is no practical assessment. The examination consists of 62 questions and two hours is allowed. The pass mark is not declared, but is around 60%.

In case you think the pass marks are high, do remember that a blindfolded man with a pin will score 25% so the mid-point is actually 62.5%, not 50%. By far the majority of the candidates pass with flying colours and those that do miss may retry as soon as they wish.

Reading the questions

At *Foundation* level the questions are straightforward. You should always read the question carefully and all four answers, even if the first or second one appears to be the right answer. You expect to see one right answer and three wrong ones. Please note, however, that the purpose of the wrong answers is to attract the attention of those candidates who are not yet ready to obtain their licence. The wrong answers should make some sense to a candidate who is not fully prepared. If you are ready for the examination you need have no fears.

At *Intermediate* level the questions will be a little more searching and expect more understanding of the subject, rather than simply regurgitating what you have been taught. Nonetheless, there are no trick questions. You may find an answer that is a true statement, but is either not answering the question asked or is trivial. For example, a transmitter that has an excessive audio input may be hard to listen to and interfere with an adjacent channel or even out of band. The fact that it may be hard to listen to is undoubtedly true, but it is trivial in comparison with the harm of causing interference.

At *Advanced* level the emphasis is on understanding and you will need to study carefully. Material from all three syllabuses will be assumed as background knowledge and much more care will be needed understanding the question. If an EMC question says "A good transmitter is being used to…" then you should take it that the transmitter is not producing spurious or harmonic radiation, is stable and on the frequency shown on the dial. The fault, if there is one, will be in its installation, proximity to other devices, field strength or some other external cause. You should also expect some questions to ask you to make a judgement as to the most probable cause. There will be a clear differentiation, so it is a fair question but the three wrong answers must appear plausible.

You may also meet questions where more than one answer is factually correct. Some may ask for the most important answer, but in all cases you should bear that matter in mind.

An example is the effect of frequency drift. Your contact will have to retune to understand you. That is a pity. You may interfere with another amateur contact, that is anti-social. You may drift outside the amateur band and interfere with a non-amateur station, that is a breach of your licence and an offence. That would be the right answer to such a question.

What if?

It may be possible to add a "what if?" to the question. A typical question might ask what callsign is given when you are using a friend's equipment rather than your own. If you are on a band and using a power available in both your and your friend's licences, you can use either your own callsign or your friend's callsign if they are supervising you. Such a question must be read carefully. The option you **MUST** use the friend's callsign is not correct, you **MAY** simply borrow the equipment and use your own callsign.

Of course, *if* your friend has a higher class of licence *and you are actually using the higher power*, then you **MUST** use your friend's callsign under their supervision. As asked, the question did not say that, so it would be wrong for you to introduce that possibility. If no such constraints are given in the question then there are none and the correct answer is that you **MAY** use either callsign.

Candidates with disabilities

There are a number of facilities to enable candidates with disabilities or learning difficulties to sit and pass the theoretical and practical elements of the overall assessment and nothing should be assumed as being a barrier. It is well understood that amateur radio is often a lifeline or a means of communication with people outside your immediate environment.

This book does not attempt to outline the facilities available; contact should be made with the examinations department at the RSGB. A medical certificate will normally be required, but its primary purpose is to provide the examination board with a guide to what is required to provide you with a fair and reasonable examination. A statement of your disability is not required, we need advice on what to do about it for you. The only feature that cannot be varied is the overall academic standard. That is common to all examination boards.

1. Amateur Radio, and
2. Licensing Conditions

You will find at the back of this book extracts from RCF booklets which are supplied when taking your examination. To enable you to answer some of the following questions you will need to refer to these pages. This is the same procedure as the examination where you will be able to refer to the RCF booklet to answer the question. You are not expected to memorise this information, although you should know your way around it. For those taking the Full licence the following questions should also be answered in conjunction with a copy of the *Terms, Conditions and Limitations* document published by Ofcom. This can be downloaded from the Ofcom website at www.ofcom.org.uk. This document also forms part of the RCF Advanced Licence booklet which will be supplied to you during the examination. This is a useful document for all amateurs as it applies to all three classes of licence.

FOUNDATION

At Foundation level the examination covers those parts of the licence that you will need to know for everyday operating. These are things such as how and when to give your callsign, which you will need to do regularly and would not have the time to check the licence for the correct procedure on each occasion.

You will need to recognise the callsigns being issued. Foundation calls begin M3 or M6 and have three letters that will be unique to you; for example M6ABC. Intermediate licensees have 2E0 and three letters and you will also hear 2E1 calls on-air. A Full licence is shown by M0 and three letters. You will hear UK calls beginning with a G on-air with the same format as M and all the number 0 - 8, but they are not examinable.

The licence clauses of key interest are 1(1)(a) and (b) on the purpose of amateur radio for self training and not for business. Clause 2(2) gives the Regional Secondary Identifiers to add to you callsign to say where in the UK you are. In Wales, for example M6ABC becomes MW6ABC. Similarly M0 becomes MW0. The 2E0 callsign format is different it becomes 2W0, the E is replaced by the appropriate letter. The full list is given in the reference section at the back.

Clause 13(1) requires you to ensure that your station is identifiable at all times and that your callsign is transmitted as frequently as practicable. That need not be on every 'over' but when first calling for a contact, a CQ call, or changing frequency or mode are obvious occasions and reasonably often thereafter.

Clauses 11(1), (2), (3) and (4)(a) detail the messages you can send and that you should not use secret codes or *broadcast*, that is just transmit to anybody listening. 1(2) allows a User Service to use your radio in an emergency and clauses 3(1) and 3(2) say you can use your callsign and that you may let another UK amateur operate under your supervision, giving your callsign. You cannot supervise a non-amateur or an overseas amateur.

Clauses 6(1) and (2) say you must notify any change of address and re-confirm at least every five years. 8(1) allows Ofcom officers the right to inspect your radio and licence. Finally, 5(1) and (2) allow Ofcom to insist you fix any problems or stop operating until you do.

The frequencies you may use are listed in Schedule 1, Table A to the licence. This shows the frequencies, the maximum transmit power and the status of amateur radio for terrestrial use or making contacts via satellites. Where amateurs are shown as 'Secondary', the Primary user has priority and you should not cause them any interference and must accept any interference they cause to your activities. In reality, you will want to move off the Primary user's frequency.

You will have a copy of the schedule to refer to, but you do need to know your way around it.

Sample Questions

The back page of the specification shows how an examination paper will be compiled. *All the Sample Questions below show the relevant syllabus section number.*

The section on licensing shows there will be six questions from the various sub-sections of the syllabus.

Question	Syllabus Item
1	1a.1, 2a.1, 2b.1
2	2c.1
3	2c.2, 2c.3, 2c.4, 2c.5
4	2c.6, 2c.7
5	2c.8
6	2c.9

f1a1-1

The main purpose of holding an amateur radio licence is to
A talk to amateur and non-amateur friends
B keep in contact with your pizza delivery fleet
C demonstrate amateur equipment on sale in a shop
D learn about communication by radio

f1a1-2

A significant feature of the amateur licence is that

A it is readily obtainable at the Post Office
B it is non-commercial in nature
C attendance at training classes is compulsory
D the Foundation licence is recognised worldwide.

f2a1-1

Which one of the items below is NOT a type of amateur licence?

A Advanced
B Foundation
C Intermediate
D Full.

f2a1-2

A Foundation licensee may design and build his or her own equipment by

A obtaining a Notice of Variation from Ofcom
B passing the Intermediate exam and upgrading their licence
C paying a fee of £20 every five years
D getting a Full licensee to certify the equipment.

f2b1-1

Which one of the call signs below indicates a Foundation licensee transmitting in Scotland?

A M6ABC/S
B MS6ABC
C M6ABC/M
D MM6ABC.

f2b1-2

A Full licensee may have the call sign

A MW0XYZ
B MD6XYZ
C MU7XYZ
D 2M1XYZ.

f2c1-1

When identifying their station an amateur should

A give their name and licence number at the start of each 'over'
B give their call sign at the beginning and end of each over
C give their location to an accuracy of at least 5km
D give their callsign as frequently as practicable.

f2c1-2

In a long contact with the same station you should give your callsign

A time the PTT is pressed
B at least once every five minutes
C at the beginning and again at the end of the contact
D often enough to be clearly identifiable while transmitting.

f2c2-1

You are speaking to M6ABC when his non-licensed sister enters the room. You

A may continue speaking as normal
B should give your callsign again
C may include the sister in the conversation
D should wait until the sister has left the room.

f2c2-2

When on the air, which action below is NOT permitted by the Foundation licence?

A Speaking to an amateur with a Full licence.
B Speaking to a French amateur.
C Speaking to a British amateur on holiday in France.
D Speaking to a close friend who is not an amateur.

f2c3-1

The use of a secret code on the air is

A only when requested by a User Service
B if you come across a person who has had an accident
C for communication within the UK only
D if you give your location correct to 5km.

f2c3-2

When talking to an amateur radio friend over the air you should NOT

A use Morse code
B use a secret code
C talk for over 15 minutes
D use more than 5W of transmit power.

f2c4-1

Which one of the actions below is NOT allowed by the Foundation licence?

A Transmitting directions to a radio club event to anybody who is listening.
B Sending practice Morse on-air to members of the local radio club.
C Discussing, on-air, an item of news heard on the TV.
D Talking for over 10 minutes without giving a callsign.

f2c4-2

Broadcasting is

A any transmission from your amateur station
B a transmission to an amateur station with whom contact has been made
C a transmission to several people in a group or net
D transmitting to anybody who happens to be listening.

f2c5-1

As a Foundation licensee you may supervise another person operating your radio, adjusting the controls and pressing the PTT if that person

A holds a UK amateur licence
B holds an amateur licence issued by a European country
C is authorised by the International Telecommunication Union (ITU)
D is a family member resident at the same address.

f2c5-2

Who may you allow to use your radio equipment under your supervision?

A Any amateur from any country provided they show their licence.
B A member of a User Service such as the ambulance service.
C Anybody who needs to send a message in an emergency.
D An officer of the Radio Society of Great Britain.

f2c6-1

If you move house you should notify Ofcom
A   at least 7 days before moving
B   immediately on moving
C   within 14 days of moving
D   before you set up your station at the new address.

f2c6-2

You should immediately inform Ofcom if you
A   receive a complaint of interference
B   discover a fault in your equipment
C   move house
D   change your transmitter.

f2c7-1

Your radio equipment may be inspected by an authorised person from
A   the BBC
B   Ofcom
C   British Telecom
D   the RSGB.

f2c7-2

You can be required to have your equipment modified on the instructions of
A   the Police
B   a radio service dealer
C   an Ofcom officer
D   a person suffering interference.

f2c8-1

The maximum transmit power permitted at a frequency of 0·1367MHz is
A   1W
B   1W erp
C   10W
D   10W erp.

f2c8-2

Communication via amateur satellite is permitted in the band
A   1·81 - 1·83MHz
B   7·00 - 7·10MHz
C   10·10 - 10·15MHz
D   14·25 - 14·35MHz.

f2c9-1

At a frequency of 145MHz you are permitted to transmit using powers up to
A   1W
B   1W erp
C   10W
D   10W erp.

f2c9-2

Operation in London is NOT permitted in the band
A   50·0 - 50·1MHz
B   430 - 431MHz
C   431 - 432MHz
D   438 - 400MHz.

INTERMEDIATE

More extracts from the licence are examined at Intermediate level, but again only those items that are likely to be in fairly regular use.

Supervision is covered in more detail, licence clause 3(2); that amateur radio cannot be used for business purposes, clause 1(1) but can be used by or to help User Services, clause 1(2). You should also remember who the User Services are, see clause 17(1)(qq).

The locations from which you may transmit are examined. These are listed in clause 2(1) as the main Station Address, an Alternative Address, a Temporary Location and Mobile. They are defined in clause 17(1). Mobile includes on a vessel, but you must be on the landward side of the low water line marked on the appropriate charts.

Unattended operation is covered by licence clauses 10(1) to 10(6) but only 10(1), (2), (3) and (6) are examined. The remote station is not for general use and the remote control link must be on amateur bands and limited to 500mW pep erp.

Log keeping is optional but clause 12(1) and (2) allow Ofcom to require a log to be kept, as may the Master of a Vessel.

Interference and remedial action is covered by clauses 7(3)-(5). You must not cause Undue Interference to other radio users and must, if asked, reduce the interference to a level satisfactory to Ofcom. This could include being restricted in transmit power, certainly possible in blocks of flats or in close proximity to the neighbours. You are also expected to carry out tests from time to time to ensure you are not causing undue interference.

Notifying Ofcom of changes of address and confirming them every five years is detailed in clauses 8(2) and 6(3), and 4(2) allows Ofcom to vary or close down a station or licence for any breaches of the licence, which includes interference that is not dealt with or failure to update the licensee's details every five years.

As in the Foundation, there will be two schedule questions, one of HF and one on VHF. The Intermediate schedule will be supplied.

Sample Questions

The Intermediate specification shows that licensing questions are selected in accordance with the table below.

Question	Syllabus Item
1	1a.1
2	2a.1 2b.1 2b.2
3	2c.1 2c.2
4	2c.3 2c.4
5	2d.1 2e.1
6	2f.1 2f.2 2f.3
7	2g.1
8	2h.1
9	2h.2

i1a1-1
Which suffix may be used when transmitting from the house of a friend?
A /P
B /A
C /M
D /T.

i1a1-2
The call 2M0XYZ/T is heard in a CQ call. It is likely that the caller is
A in Scotland but is using the wrong suffix
B in Scotland at a temporary location such an hotel
C on the Isle of Man but is using the wrong suffix
D on the Isle of Man at a temporary location such as an hotel.

i2a1-1
When operating at a campsite under the supervision of a Full licensee, the call sign to be used is
A one's own call sign with the suffix /S
B the call sign of the supervisor
C the call sign of the supervisor with the suffix /S
D the call sign of the owner of the equipment being used.

i2a1-2
When operating a friend's equipment at their house, the callsign used
A must be your own callsign
B must be your own callsign with the suffix /A
C must be that of the friend
D may be either your or your friend's callsign.

i2b1-1
Which activity below is NOT permitted by the amateur licence?
A Giving details of the amateur club programme to club members.
B Keeping in contact with a number of pizza delivery staff.
C Advising of personal radio equipment for sale.
D Talking to a group of more than 12 participants.

i2b1-2
The licence allows amateur radio to be used
A to advise another amateur how to get to the local amateur radio dealer
B by an amateur radio dealer to advertise equipment for sale
C to control a fleet of taxis available for hire
D by a telephone engineer to call his office.

i2b2-1
Which organisation below is NOT a User Service?
A The police
B The St John Ambulance Brigade
C Raynet
D Women's Royal Voluntary Service.

i2b2-2
The licence permits you to assist a User Service by
A only passing messages for them in an emergency
B only passing messages for them in an emergency or on an exercise
C only passing messages or allowing them to pass messages in an emergency
D passing messages or allowing them to pass messages in an emergency or an exercise.

i2c1-1
You correctly call CQ on the 2 metre calling channel and your friend answers saying 145.525MHz is clear. When moving to that frequency you must
A call CQ again expecting your friend to answer
B give your callsign again
C give your friend's callsign
D wait until your friend calls you.

i2c2-1
A Temporary Location is defined as
A a fixed postal address in the UK other than the Main Station Address
B being on the person of the Licensee in the UK when not at the Main Station Address
C a location used for transmissions lasting not longer than 15 minutes
D a fixed location in the UK other than the Main Station Address or an Alternative Address.

i2c2-2
When operating from an hotel room on holiday in the UK, you are operating from
A a portable location
B a temporary location
C an alternative location
D a specified location.

i2c3-1
Operation of an amateur transmitter is not licensed from a
A taxi
B bus
C train
D plane.

i2c3-2
An Intermediate licensee may NOT operate on a vessel
A on a lake or inland loch
B on a river that is affected by the tides
C on the seaward side of the low water line
D except when in international waters.

i2c4-1
The Intermediate licence permits operation
A only in the UK
B in the UK and European Economic Community
C any CEPT T/R 61-01 signatory country
D the UK and Commonwealth.

i2c4-2

An Intermediate amateur may expect to be allowed to operate from

A France

B any country with a sea border with the UK

C any European country

D the United Kingdom only.

i2d1-1

The Intermediate licence permits the Unattended Operation of a Beacon for

A propagation experimental purposes only

B direction finding competitions only

C both direction finding and propagation experiments

D any purpose provided the transmit power is limited to 500mW.

i2d1-2

When using a radio link to remotely control the main transmitter, the link equipment is limited to a transmit power of

A 10mW

B 500mW

C 5W

D that of the band used by the main transmitter.

i2e1-1

You may be required to keep a Log of your transmissions by

A a person authorised by Ofcom

B the police

C a person complaining of interference

D a radio and TV service dealer.

i2e1-2

The time for which you may be required by an Ofcom inspector to keep a Log of your transmissions is

A not more than 30 days

B two months

C six months

D whatever specified.

i2f1-1

The licence requires you to avoid causing any undue interference to

A any electronic equipment

B any wireless telegraphy

C equipment meeting the terms of IR2028

D equipment compliant with the EMC directive.

i2f2-1

If interference occurs to a neighbours television you may be required to reduce emissions to

A whatever level prevents interference

B the level specified in the EMC Directive

C the degree satisfactory to Ofcom

D the level in CEPT T/R 61-01.

i2f3-1

How often must you check that your radio equipment is not causing undue interference?

A every three months

B from time to time

C whenever a complaint is received

D during an inspection.

i2g1-1

You must confirm your licence details

A from time to time

B annually

C every five years

D only when they change.

i2g1-2

Your licence is liable to revocation

A if a complaint of interference is received

B if interference is traced to your station

C if you fail to confirm your details when due

D for non-payment of the licence fee.

i2h1-1

Which part of the 14MHz amateur band is NOT permitted for use in satellite communications?

A 14·00 - 14·25MHz

B 14·00 - 14·35MHz

C 14·20 - 14·30MHz

D 14·25 - 14·35MHz.

i2h1-2

The schedule to the licence shows

A how the International Amateur Radio Union (IARU) has chosen to use the amateur bands

B the frequency bands allocated for amateur use within the United Kingdom

C how the different users of radio services share the radio frequency spectrum

D the types of use to which radio amateurs are permitted to put their frequency bands.

i2h2-1

The frequency 431·50MHz is subject to a transmit power limit of

A 32W

B 40W

C 40W erp

D 50W.

i2h2-2

Which frequency band is restricted to transmissions from Space to Earth for satellite operation?

A 1260-1270MHz

B 2400-2450MHz

C 5650-5670MHz

D 5830-5850MHz.

ADVANCED

At Advanced level it is assumed that you are familiar with all the regularly used parts of the licence and the examination covers those items that are new to this level, or are likely only to be of interest if you decide to get involved in that particular facet; supervising trainees for example. In normal use you would check the licence before proceeding, and so it is here.

The Full licence document is available to you and you will need to know your way around it. Some questions, such as the power level permitted for unattended operation are not simply given in Schedule 1, Table C, there are additional restrictions in Schedule 2, which it is easy to miss! You really must know the licence quite well, but you must also take care to look up the answers carefully.

Sample Questions

The relevant table from the Advanced specification shows that there are 10 questions to be answered.

Question	Syllabus Item
1	2a.1
2	2b.1
3	2c.1
4	2d.1
5	2e.1
6	2f.1
7	2g.1
8	2h.1
9	2i.1
10	2j.1

a2a1-1
The callsign GU1ABC indicates the amateur
A has been licensed by the German authorities
B holds a UK licence and is operating from the Channel Islands
C has been issued with a Foundation licence
D is operating in Unattended mode.

a2a1-2
When giving your location a recommended method is to give
A the IARU locator in the format AB12xy
B a grid reference in the format AB1234
C the name of a town within 10km
D the first three or four characters of the postcode.

a2b1-1
You are assisting a User Service that has been called to an accident. A member of the public approaches you asking you to call the User Service to see if a named individual has been taken to hospital. You should
A call the User Service direct
B call an amateur station co-located with the User Service
C ask for the request to be put in writing
D refuse to pass such a message.

a2b1-2
During a disaster which has occurred in another country, you may
A communicate with a non-amateur station
B hear non-amateur stations on amateur bands
C communicate with amateur stations in the disaster area only if you are a member of Raynet or similar organisation
D receive a compulsory instruction to close down from the International Telecommunication Union (ITU).

a2c1-1
A Recognised Training Course is any course which must
A have been registered with the RSGB RCE Department
B be held in premises accredited for holding examinations
C if successfully completed, result in a Radio Amateurs' Examination Pass Certificate
D be run by a properly accredited instructor holding a Full Amateur Licence.

a2c1-2
To supervise a person operating who holds a recognised Radio Amateurs' Examination Pass Certificate but has not applied for a licence, the supervisor must hold
A a Foundation licence
B an Intermediate licence
C a Full licence
D a Full licence and be a registered instructor.

a2d1-1
When operating in accordance with your licence on a Vessel at Sea, the master of the vessel may require you to
1 send a message to a maritime radio station
2 close down on demand
3 keep a Log of your transmissions
A 1 and 2 only
B 2 only
C 2 and 3 only
D 1, 2 and 3.

a2d1-2
When Maritime Mobile inside the territorial waters of Australia you should operate only
A on the frequencies in your UK schedule that are also assigned in ITU region 3
B on the frequencies given in the Australian amateur licence
C on the frequencies that are in both the UK and Australian amateur licences
D if you also hold a licence issued by the Australian authorities.

a2e1-1
When operating under the terms of CEPT T/R 61-01 a breach of the rules in the host country is
A only a breach of their rules
B only a breach of your UK licence, unless you also hold a licence from the host country
C a breach of the conditions of the CEPT agreement
D a breach of both the UK and host country licence conditions.

a2f1-1

M0ABC calls you and asks you to record and retransmit a message to G4XYZ. You should

A decline the request since the licence does not permit third party messages except on behalf of a User Service

B retransmit the message but omit the callsign of the originator because you are now transmitting the message

C ensure that if you retransmit the originator's callsign, the origin of the message and retransmission are clear

D retransmit the message as received, including the originator's callsign and omit your own since it is not your message.

a2f1-2

Often when helping a User Service it is convenient to use a "tactical callsign" such as the name of your checkpoint or role. This device

A is simply regarded by your licence as part of a message

B may be used instead of the call sign in section one of your licence

C must be given on every 'over' if not using your licence callsign

D must be accompanied by your licence callsign every time it is used.

a2g1-1

When setting up the station M0XYZ to be operated by remote control, it must

A be available for use by any UK licensed amateur

B be failsafe such that any failure will not result in unintended transmission

C have a control link limited to a maximum power of 500mW pep e.r.p.

D automatically transmit its call sign each time it is accessed.

a2g1-2

The control link to a remotely controlled main transmitter must be

A encrypted to prevent misuse by others

B adequately secure to ensure compliance with clause 3 of the licence

C limited to frequencies in the amateur bands above 30MHz

D able to be used by a nominated back-up operator in case of malfunction.

a2h1-1

You may be required to keep a Log of your transmissions by

A a person suffering undue interference

B the master of a vessel on which you are operating

C a local authority environmental services officer

D a police officer in uniform.

a2h1-2

When transmitting television pictures you should identify your station by means of

A a voice announcement on the accompanying sound channel

B a placard or electronic picture showing your callsign in writing

C a Morse or voice announcement centred on the video carrier

D a Morse or voice announcement centred on the transmitted bandwidth.

a2i1-1

The emissions from your transmitter should be controlled such that

A not more than 1% of the mean power falls outside the bands defined in the schedule to the licence

B not more than 1% of the mean power falls outside the nominal modulated carrier bandwidth

C the emitted frequency is as stable and as free from Unwanted Emissions as defined in Interface Requirement IR2028

D its use does not cause any interference to any wireless telegraphy, telephony or video transmission.

a2i1-2

If a person authorised by Ofcom is of the opinion that an urgent situation exists then your Radio Equipment may be inspected at

A any time of the day or night

B and any and all reasonable times

C during office hours but 7 days a week

D at any time by appointment.

a2j1-1

Peak Envelope Power is that power supplied to the antenna

A at the peak of an RF cycle during normal operation

B averaged over 1 RF cycle at the crest of the modulation

C averaged over 1 audio cycle on an RMS power meter

D by a steady carrier before it is modulated.

a2j1-2

The maximum transmit power of an unattended beacon operating at a frequency of 70·030MHz is

A 25W

B 32W

C 100W

D 160W.

3. Technical Basics

This section covers basic electricity, current, potential difference, power, resistance and frequency. Current is the rate of flow of electrons in a conductor. It is measured in Amperes, which is shortened to Amps (A). The Potential Difference (PD) gives the energy transferred by a given quantity of electrical charge as it flows through a device. A higher PD means that more energy is being transferred by that same quantity of electrical charge. Potential difference is measured in Volts, symbol V.

Power is a measure of the rate at which energy is being transferred and is measured in Watts (W). A 2kW kettle will heat water twice as fast as a 1kW kettle.

The power is related to the current and PD by the formula:

$$P = V \times I$$

...that is the power (P) in Watts (W) is the product of the current I amps and the PD V volts.

Resistance is an electrical property of a material. It results in a current through the material transferring heat energy to the material. In a thin wire filament in a light bulb, for example, the electrons are much more likely to interact with the atoms so the chance of transferring energy is much greater. The wire gets very hot. We say the wire has more resistance. A thicker wire of the same material and the same length has more spaces between the atoms so the electrons have a smaller chance of transferring energy to them. This wire has a lower resistance. Resistance is measured in Ohms, symbol Ω.

Other materials, which are not as good a conductor, will have a higher resistance.

The resistance of a device is given by the formula:

$$R = V/I$$

where V is the PD in volts across the device and I is the current in amps flowing through it. R is the resistance in ohms, Ω.

At Foundation level, any calculations required will be using the basic unit, but in real life the values may vary over a much larger range. We need to know the milli, which is a thousandth of the unit, eg 10mA is ten one thousandths of an amp, and 1000mA = 1A. We also need the kilo: 2kV is 2000 volts and the Mega: 3MΩ is 3,000,000 ohms.

A simple circuit

The circuit diagram in **Fig 3.1** shows a battery on the left, a bulb on the right, and the connections. The arrow shows the direction of current flow. If the battery has a PD of 6V and 0·5A is flowing, the power drawn from the battery and transferred to heat and light in the bulb is:

$$P = V \times I = 6 \times 0·5 = 3W.$$

The resistance of the bulb is $R = V/I = 6/0 \times 5 = 12\Omega$.

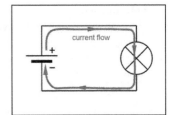
current flow
+
−

Fig 3.1. A simple circuit.

DC and AC

Direct Current, DC. To start thinking about circuits we begin by imagining that a current flows from the positive terminal of a battery, around the circuit and then back to the negative terminal of the battery. Filament bulbs do not mind which way the current flows but other devices may be damaged if the current flows in the wrong direction. We must connect the battery the right way round, that is we must connect it with the correct 'polarity'.

Alternating Current, AC. What would happen in a circuit if we reversed the battery and then put it back the right way again? The current would first flow one way and then back the other. This is called alternating current or AC. The mains supply to the house is AC, it is easier to generate and distribute. Audio and radio frequency signals are AC and the rate at which the polarity changes is called the frequency of the AC.

The mains changes at a rate of 50 cycles or complete changes per second, correctly know as 50Hz. 1Hz is one cycle per second.

We can hear frequencies down to about 100Hz. Lower frequencies are felt as much as heard. The highest audible frequency is around 15kHz. For communications the range 300Hz to 3kHz is normally considered sufficient.

Radio frequencies, RF, are much higher. Medium frequencies (MF), which includes the medium wave (MW) broadcast band, are 300kHz to 3MHz, high frequencies (HF) 3MHz to 30MHz, and very high frequencies (VHF) 30MHz to 300MHz. Ultra high frequencies (UHF) are 300MHz to 3000MHz (3000MHz is often written as 3GHz).

Sample Questions

There are four questions on technical basics. One on units and the formulae for power and resistance; one on polarity, circuits, symbols and the meaning of DC and AC; and two questions covering different frequencies, both audio and RF, and frequency to wavelength conversion.

Question	Syllabus Item
7	3a.1, 3b.1, 3b.2, 3b.3
8	3b.4, 3b.5, 3b.6, 3b7
9 & 10	3c.1, 3c.2, 3c.3

f3a1-1

The unit of resistance and the symbol used are

A   ohms, symbol O
B   ohms, symbol Ω
C   watts, symbol W
D   watts, symbol P.

f3a1-2

A current of 23000mA should normally be written as

A   2·3A
B   23A
C   0·23kA
D   23,000mA.

f3b1-1

A flow of current in an insulator is

A   the movement of electrons
B   the movement of neutrons
C   not normally possible
D   only possible with DC.

f3b1-2

Which one of the materials is a conductor?

A   Brass
B   Ceramic
C   Plastic
D   Rubber.

f3b2-1

If the power P and supply voltage (potential difference) V of a torch bulb are known, the current I drawn may be found using the formula

A $I = P/V$
B $I = V/P$
C $I = P \times V$
D $I = P + V$.

f3b2-2

A radio transmitter runs from 12V and draws a current of 2A. What is the power supplied to the radio?

A   6W
B   12W
C   14W
D   24W.

f3b2-3

A travel hair dryer is marked 120V, 720W. When operating the current drawn will be

A   6W
B   6A
C   12W
D   12A.

f3b3-1

The drawing shows a battery connected to a bulb via a resistor R. Increasing the value of R will

A   make the bulb glow brighter
B   reduce the brilliance of the bulb
C   have no effect on the brightness of the bulb
D   cause the bulb to 'blow'.

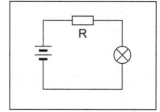

f3b3-2

A car headlamp is drawing 6A from a 12V supply. The resistance of the headlamp is

A   0·5Ω (½Ω)
B   2Ω
C   6Ω
D   18Ω.

f3b3-3

The mains supply is 230V. An electric kettle is plugged in which has a resistance of 23Ω, what current will flow?

A   10A
B   23A
C   230A
D   253A.

f3b4-1

The drawing shows a battery in a battery holder and a bulb. In order to make the bulb light it is necessary to make wire connections from

A   point 1 to point 2
B   point 1 to point 3
C   point 1 to point 2 and point 3 to point 4
D   point 1 to point 3 and point 2 to point 4.

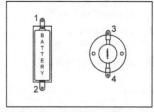

f3b5-1

The battery is inserted the wrong way round in a small torch, which has a filament bulb, but a connection is made. The torch will

A   work perfectly well
B   not work until the battery is replaced the right way round
C   not work until the battery is turned round and the bulb is replaced
D   get very hot and possibly catch fire.

f3b6-1

If the polarity of a power supply is continuously changing then it is known as

A   a DC supply

B   an AC supply

C   an HF supply

D   an audio supply.

f3b7-1

The symbol shown in the drawing is a

A   fuse

B   resistor

C   cell or battery

D   switch.

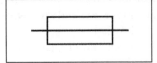

f3b7-2

The drawing is the circuit symbol for a

A   bulb

B   antenna

C   microphone

D   earth.

f3c1-1

For amateur radio communication purposes the range of audio frequencies required is about

A   50Hz

B   100Hz to 15kHz

C   300Hz to 3kHz

D   3MHz to 30MHz.

f3c1-2

The frequency of an audio signal will tell us how many cycles occur in 1 second. 600 cycles a second is normally shown as

A   600c/s

B   600Hz

C   600RF

D   600W.

f3c2-1

The frequency 106MHz is used for

A   amateur radio

B   broadcasting

C   land mobile radio

D   space operations.

f3c3-1

The wavelength corresponding to a frequency of 10MHz is

A   10m

B   30m

C   50m

D   100m.

f3c3-2

An old radio receiver has its tuning dial marked in wavelength. When set to a wavelength of 40m, the frequency will be about

A   3MHz

B   7MHz

C   15MHz

D   70MHz.

INTERMEDIATE

At Intermediate level a wider range of unit prefixes must be known, from pico to Giga and calculations are likely to involve the milli and kilo. The full range of prefixes is shown in the Reference section at the back.

Series and parallel circuits

In **Fig 3.2**, R1 and R2 are in series. To find their total resistance, use the formula $R_{tot} = R1 + R2$.

R3 and R4 are in parallel. If they have the same value, the total will be R3/2 (or R4/2). In general for 'n' equal resistors in parallel, the formula is R/n.

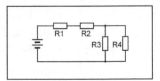

Fig 3.2. A series and parallel circuit.

The supply is shown as two cells in series to form a battery. The energy is stored in chemical form, converted to electrical energy when a current is drawn. In the resistors, this energy will be transferred into heat.

Capacitors and inductors

A capacitor comprises two conducting plates separated by an insulator, the dielectric as shown in **Fig 3.3**.

If the two plates are connected to a battery, a momentary current will flow. The capacitor has stored a charge of electricity. The energy required to do that is stored in the electric field between the plates.

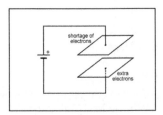

Fig 3.3. A parallel plate capacitor.

If the area of the plates, their separation or the nature of the material between them (the dielectric) changes the ability to store a charge, its capacitance, has changed.

An inductor is a coil of wire and is shown in **Fig 3.4**. When a current flows in the coil a magnetic field is formed round the coil. This requires some energy, which is stored in the magnetic field.

Changing the number of turns, diameter and spacing of the coil will alter the field and the amount of energy stored. The energy stored for a given

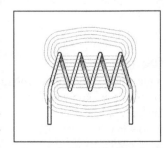

Fig 3.4. An inductor and its magnetic field.

current is related to the 'inductance' of the coil, so the inductance depends on the number of turns and dimensions.

Alternating currents and voltages

The supply from a battery has a constant polarity. Current flows in one direction and is termed Direct Current, DC. An Alternating Current, AC, supply keeps changing its polarity and the current changes its direction of flow in response. This is shown graphically in **Fig 3.5**. The waveform is known as a sine wave. To describe fully a sine wave both the amplitude and the time

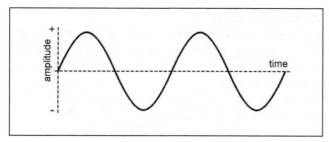

Fig 3.5. Two cycles of a sine wave.

for 1 cycle, the periodic time, or the number of cycles per second, the frequency in Hertz (Hz), must be specified.

If this waveform of PD and Current is applied to a resistor the heating effect will change as the voltage and current rises, falls, stops, and then repeats again in the other direction. We can 'smooth out' these variations by using what are called the RMS values of PD and current. RMS values are special because they give the same heating effect as a DC supply.

The peak and RMS values are related by:

$$V_{RMS} = \frac{V_{PEAK}}{\sqrt{2}} \qquad \sqrt{2} = 1\cdot414.$$

Reactance and Impedance

If a sine wave supply is applied to a capacitor, the capacitor will alternately charge, discharge and charge again with opposite polarity. Energy is being stored and released in the process. The PD across the capacitor depends on the charge, and the capacitance of the capacitor.

The quantity $\dfrac{V_{RMS}}{I_{RMS}} = X_C \ \Omega$

X_C is the reactance of the capacitor and is measured in Ω.

AC applied to an inductor will cause the magnetic field to build up and collapse in alternate directions. The energy storage and release will again result in a PD across the inductor and, as for the capacitor, the ratio of V_{RMS} to I_{RMS} gives the reactance of the coil X_L measured in ohms.

If a capacitor or inductor are in series with a resistor, as shown in **Fig 3.6**, there will be a PD across the resistor and a separate PD across the capacitor or inductor. The ratio of V_R to I, is, of course, the *resistance* R of the resistor, $V_R/I = R$. The ratio V_C or V_L to I is the *reactance* of the capacitor or inductor. The ratio of the overall supply voltage V to I is known as the *impedance* of the circuit. Impedance is also measured in ohms. Impedance is a combination of resistance and reactance.

In the resistor, the energy is transferred to heat but in the capacitor or inductor the energy is simply stored over one part of the cycle and released in the next.

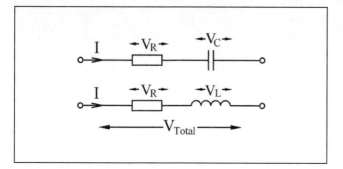

Fig 3.6. A resistor in series with a capacitor or inductor.

Capacitor and Inductor - Resonance

If a capacitor (C) and inductor (L) are connected together, as shown in **Fig 3.7**, and if there are no losses, losing energy as heat (impossible in practice), then the energy can flow back and forth indefinitely. The rate at which this happens is called the resonant frequency and this frequency is dependent on the size of C and L. Larger values of either C or L cause the energy to take longer to transfer and reduce the resonant frequency.

If C and L are in series, the circuit will readily allow a current, at the resonant fre-

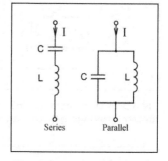

Fig 3.7. A capacitor and inductor in series and parallel resonant circuits.

quency, to pass. The circuit presents a low impedance. Away from resonance the impedance is much higher.

If C and L are in parallel, the circuit will not allow an external current to pass and the circuit presents a high impedance at the resonant frequency. Away from resonance the impedance is much lower.

Transformers

Fig 3.8 shows a transformer of two coils sharing the same magnetic field. The laminated iron core enhances the field and ensures the whole field is shared. Energy may be transferred from one coil to another via the field, but only with AC. With DC there is no change in the field and no energy transfer.

If the secondary has more turns than the primary, a higher PD is available. With fewer secondary turns, a lower PD is produced. The power at the secondary will be the same as at the primary, neglecting any power lost as heat in the transformer. A step up in PD must mean a lower available current. More often amateurs need to step the mains down to 12 - 16V and now the primary current will be lower than the secondary current.

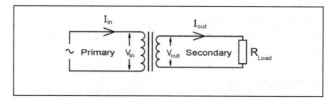

Fig 3.8. A transformer

Diodes and a power supply

The transformer can step the 230V mains down to a voltage suitable for a 13·8V DC transceiver. Its output is still AC and must be changed to DC using a diode. This is shown in **Fig 3.9**. This is now unidirectional but is still unsuitable to power a transceiver.

A capacitor can store a charge while the diode is conducting and release it during the time when the diode is not conducting. However, in supplying energy its own PD will fall. The capacitor must be able to hold sufficient charge that its PD does not fall significantly. This is shown in **Fig 3.10**.

In a light emitting diode (LED) the construction is such that visible or infrared light is emitted when current is flowing. The variable capacitance diode is used reverse biased and

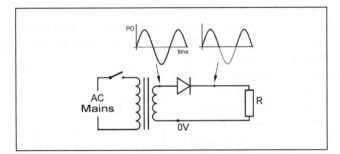

Fig 3.9. A transformer, diode and load resistor. The transformer provides AC, the diode rectifies it to pulsed DC.

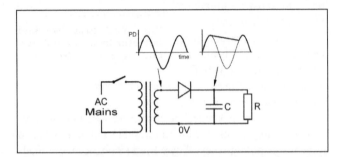

Fig 3.10. The capacitor smoothes out the pulsed DC to provide a more constant PD.

non-conducting. It can then behave as a small capacitor and the magnitude of the reverse bias will alter the capacitance.

Transistors

A transistor circuit is shown in **Fig 3.11**. A small variation in the base current, I_B, will result in a larger change in the collector current, I_C. The transistor has *gain* (β) and the size of the gain is given by $\beta = I_C / I_B$. By this means a small signal at the base becomes a larger signal at the collector and the transistor has *amplified* the signal. To do so correctly, the values of the resistors must be correctly chosen and this is called correct *biasing* of the transistor.

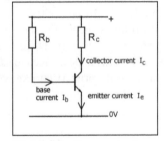

Fig 3.11. Currents in a transistor.

With larger changes in the base current, the collector current can vary from zero to the maximum the circuit can supply. The transistor then appears to be acting as a switch.

A simple amplifier circuit is shown in **Fig 3.12**.

If the transistor is used with an LC tuned circuit or a crystal, the transistor can maintain the oscillations in the tuned circuit so the device provides a continuous signal at the resonant frequency. This may be audio or radio frequencies. The crystal exhibits a very high Q-factor and provides a stable output frequency. An LC tuned circuit is continuously variable but does not provide the same accuracy or frequency stability.

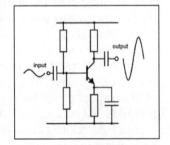

Fig 3.12. A transistor amplifier circuit.

Measurements

Fig 3.13 shows two multimeters being used to measure the current and voltage (PD) in a circuit. The voltmeter is connected across or in parallel with the circuit but the ammeter must be inserted in a break in the circuit. The ammeter may be inserted at any

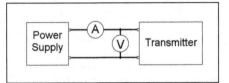

Fig 3.13. Measurement of power by multiplying the voltage and current.

point in the circuit and the same reading will result. The same PD will be observed across the battery or the transmitter.

By multiplying the voltage and current readings, the power supplied by the battery can be found. The RF output power of the transmitter will be rather less than this because some power is used to run the internal circuits and to provide the front panel displays.

Sample Questions

The Intermediate table shows there are eight questions on Technical Basics.

Question	Syllabus Item
10	3a.1 3c.1
11	3b.1
12	3d.1 3d.2 3d.3 3e.1
13	3f.1 3f.2 3f.3 3f.4
14	3g.1 3g.2 3g.3
15	3h.1 3h.2 3i.1 3i.2 3i.3 3i.4
16	3i.5 3i.6 3i.7 3i.8
17	3j.1 3j.2 3j.3 3j.4 3j.5

i3a1-1

85,000,000,000nA should properly be written as

A   85mA

B   85,000mA

C   8·5A

D   85A.

i3b1-1

The drawing shows two resistors in series fed from a 12V battery. R1 is 4Ω, R2 is 8Ω. What is the power dissipated in the 4Ω resistor?

A   4W.

B   8W.

C   12W.

D   28W.

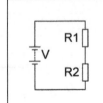

i3b1-2

What is the effective resistance of the two resistors in parallel in the diagram?

A   28kΩ.
B   30kΩ.
C   58kΩ.
D   112kΩ.

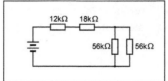

i3b1-3

The circuit diagram shows a 10V battery feeding two series resistors. What is the voltage across the 2Ω resistor?

A   2V.
B   3V.
C   4V.
D   6V.

i3b1-4

A 12V battery supplies a 2Ω resistor and a 4Ω resistor connected in series. What power is dissipated in the 4Ω resistor?

A   8W.
B   12W.
C   16W.
D   24W.

i3c1-1

A reversible chemical process is a feature of a

A   primary cell
B   secondary cell
C   diode
D   crystal.

i3d1-1

The drawing shows a

A   capacitor
B   inductor
C   diode
D   switch.

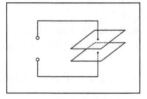

i3d2-1

Increasing the area of the plates of a capacitor will

A   increase the breakdown voltage
B   decrease the breakdown voltage
C   increase its ability to store a charge
D   decrease its polarity.

i3d3-1

Larger capacitors are often of electrolytic construction and are

A   normally polarised
B   unable to pass alternating currents
C   fitted either way round
D   unsuitable for smoothing circuits.

i3e1-1

The circuit component which consists of a single coil of wire is

A   an inductor
B   a capacitor
C   a transformer
D   an antenna.

i3e1-2

An inductor relies of the fact that when a current passes through a wire it

A   increases in temperature
B   forms a magnetic field
C   limits to current to a set value
D   oscillates at a known frequency.

i3e1-3

What does an inductor store in its magnetic field?

A   Current
B   Potential difference
C   Energy
D   Power.

i3f1-1

The drawing shows two cycles of a sine wave. If the frequency is 50Hz, the time for the TWO cycles is

A   20mS
B   30mS
C   40mS
D   50mS.

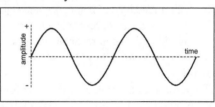

i3f1-2

The waveform shows the PD across a resistive circuit. The power dissipated in the circuit will be a maximum

A   at all times during the cycle
B   at point 1 but minimum at 3
C   at points 1 and 3
D   at point 2.

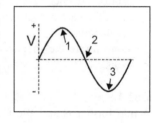

i3f2-1

An alternating current can pass through a capacitor because

A   capacitors always block direct currents
B   it continuously charges and discharges
C   allows electrons to pass through the dielectric
D   has a permeable membrane dielectric.

i3f3-1

If an alternating current (I) is passed through an inductor, there will be a potential difference (V) across it. The ratio V/I will give the

A   resistance of the inductor in ohms
B   reactance of the inductor in ohms
C   reactance of the inductor in henries
D   inductance of the inductor in henries.

i3f4-1

The drawing shows an inductor and resistor in series. When an alternating PD is applied, energy will be transferred into heat in

A   resistor and inductor
B   only in the resistor
C   only in the inductor
D   neither of the components.

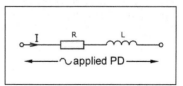

i3g1-1

The circuit shown is usually called

A a resistive circuit

B an inductive circuit

C a tuned circuit

D a dielectric circuit.

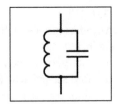

i3g2-1

The resonant frequency of a circuit containing a capacitor and inductor depends on

A the frequency of the applied signal

B the amount of energy contained in the capacitor

C the values of the capacitor and inductor

D only the value of the capacitor.

i3g3-1

A series resonant circuit has a

A low impedance at resonance and accepts a current flow

B high impedance at resonance and rejects current flow

C low impedance at resonance and rejects a current flow

D high impedance at resonance and accepts a current flow.

i3h1-1

The purpose of the iron core in a transformer is to

A provide a substantial support to wind the coils on

B allow both coils to be placed side by side but insulated from each other

C limit the energy transferred from one coil to the other to a safe value

D concentrate the magnetic field present round both the coils.

i3h2-1

A transformer is suitable for transferring energy from the primary winding to the secondary winding

A only when alternating currents are used

B only when direct currents are used

C when either direct or alternating currents are used

D provided both windings are wound in the same direction.

i3h2-2

The drawing shows a transformer used to reduce the 230V mains supply to 12V. The secondary winding will have

A fewer turns than the primary winding

B more turns than the primary winding

C the same number of turns as the primary

D a direct current (DC) output.

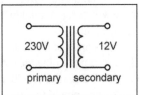

i3i1-1

The drawing shows a diode and resistor connected across a battery. The voltage across the resistor will be about

A 0V

B 5·0V

C 9·3V

D 10V.

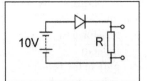

i3i1-2

A 12V battery powered transmitter is to be run from the mains. A suitable power supply will contain a transformer and a

A resistor

B inductor

C diode

D transistor.

i3i1-3

The drawing shows a power supply circuit and four waveforms that might be seen at different points in the circuit. Which waveforms would be seen at points 1 and 2?

	Point 1	Point 2
A	Waveform A	B
B	Waveform A	C
C	Waveform B	C
D	Waveform B	D.

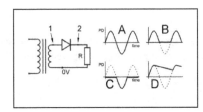

i3i2-1

One of the problems of using a diode to rectify the AC from a transformer is that there is no output during the negative half cycles of the AC. This can be solved by using a

A diode

B capacitor

C transistor

D tuned circuit.

i3i3-1

A particular feature of an LED is that it

A produces heat and light when a filament glows white hot

B is made from a material that produces light when passing DC

C produces light only when passing AC

D can amplify the input light to make it brighter.

i3i4-1

When the device shown has its input voltage 'V' varied, the

A current through the resistor will change

B voltage between 'A' and 'B' will remain constant

C capacitance between 'A' and 'B' will vary

D forward bias on the diode will change.

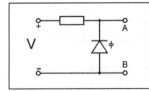

i3i5-1

The transistor in the circuit diagram is there to

A limit the current through the resistors

B remove any unwanted signals

C produce DC from the AC input

D amplify the input signal.

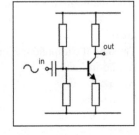

i3i5-2

A particular feature of a transistor amplifier is that a small change in the

A   collector current can cause a large change in base voltage

B   collector voltage can cause a large change in the emitter current

C   base current can cause a large change in the collector current

D   emitter current can cause a large change in the collector current.

i3i5-3

The parameter β of a transistor relates to its gain, that is the ratio of the

A   collector current to emitter current

B   collector voltage base voltage

C   collector current to base current

D   emitter current to collector current.

i3i6-1

The circuit shows a relay being controlled by a transistor that is being used as a switch. To achieve this the

A   input signal should be greater than that required for an amplifier

B   input signal should be less than that required for an amplifier

C   biasing should be such that the transistor is always fully conducting

D   biasing should be such that the transistor is always non-conducting.

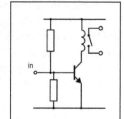

i3i7-1

Biasing a transistor is

A   ensuring the input signal will not cause an overload

B   supplying the correct DC voltages and currents

C   setting the frequency of oscillation to the correct value

D   applying a signal to squelch the audio when required.

i3i8-1

The function of the transistor in an oscillator is to

A   set the correct DC voltages

B   determine the frequency of oscillation

C   maintain the oscillations in the tuned circuit

D   vary the value of the capacitance of the tuned circuit.

i3i8-2

The diagram shows an oscillator, normally called a

A   crystal oscillator

B   adjustable frequency oscillator

C   variable frequency oscillator

D   modulation frequency oscillator.

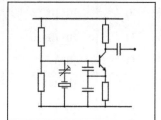

i3j1-1

The drawing shows a meter connected in a circuit to perform a measurement. The meter should be set to read

A   10V DC with terminal 1 positive

B   20V DC with terminal 1 positive

C   20A DC with terminal 2 positive

D   10A DC with terminal 2 negative.

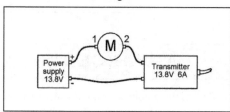

i3j2-1

A meter scale is shown in the drawing. The meter is set to read 10V full scale. The measured voltage is

A   1·23V

B   6·0V

C   6·3V

D   10·0V.

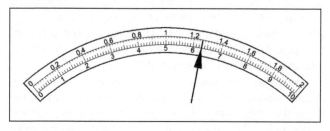

i3j3-1

In the circuit shown the meters are correctly shown in which line of the table below?

	1	2	3
A	A	A	V.
B	A	V	V.
C	V	V	V.
D	V	A	A.

V = voltmeter

A = ammeter

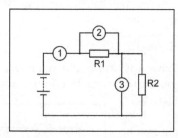

i3j4-1

In the circuit shown, which two meters will have the same reading?

A   Meters 1 and 2.

B   Meters 1 and 4.

C   Meters 2 and 3.

D   Meters 3 and 4.

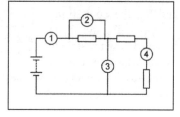

i3j5-1

The ammeter in the drawing reads 3A when on transmit. A reasonable RF transmit power will be

A 5W
B 15W
C 50W
D 100W.

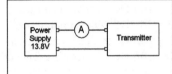

ADVANCED

At Advanced level the emphasis is much more on understanding and application of the knowledge you have gained. It is likely that the questions will be slanted differently to the way in which you were taught, although they will, of course, still be covered by the syllabus.

PD and EMF

The difference between PD and EMF is related to the source impedance or resistance. A 'perfect' battery can provide any amount of current and maintain its terminal voltage. The voltage of a real battery will droop and this is due to the internal resistance of the battery, partly ohmic resistance and partly limits to the chemical processes. The EMF is the open circuit voltage and the PD is the terminal voltage on-load or a voltage measured anywhere else in a circuit.

Antennas have source resistances, numerically identical to radiation resistance, so loading the antenna will cause its terminal voltage to drop. Maximum power transfer occurs when source and load resistances are equal and under those conditions the terminal PD will be halved. It is necessary to be sure which figure is being quoted or used.

Resistors in parallel

Advanced questions may have resistors of any value. The formula is:

$$\frac{1}{R_{Total}} = \frac{1}{R_1} + \frac{1}{R_2} + \frac{1}{R_3} \text{ etc.}$$

For just two resistors in parallel, this simplifies to:

$$R_{Total} = \frac{R_1 \times R_2}{R_1 + R_2}$$

Fig 3.14 shows a typical circuit you might be asked to analyse. First you must work out the effective resistance of R_2 and R_3, then that resistance is in series with R_1. The current can now be calculated, giving the PD dropped across R_1 and thus the voltage across R_2 and R_3, thereby giving the current through them. It is also now possible to calculate the power in any of the resistors using either the V and I for each separate resistor or using the formula:

$$P = \frac{V^2}{R} \text{ or } P = I^2 R$$

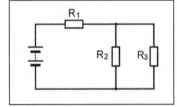

Fig 3.14. Series and parallel resistors.

Potential Divider

Fig 3.15 shows a potential divider. It is simply two resistors in series, but used to obtain a specific voltage, perhaps to bias the base of a transistor. The supply voltage is divided in the ratio of the two resistors, provided the current drawn is low compared to the standing current through R_1 and R_2. To avoid numerical errors you should always estimate the answer before calculating it. That way silly answers due to an arithmetic error can be spotted and avoided.

The formula is:

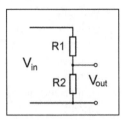

Fig 3.15. A potential divider.

$$V_{out} = V_{in} \times \frac{R_2}{R_1 + R_2}$$

Decibels

The decibel is a scientific unit of measurement. It is a unit of ratio, not absolute magnitude. Consider the frequency to wavelength conversion chart in the Reference section. The scales are logarithmic. The same space is used to cover 1 to 10 and 10 to 100 or 100 to 1000. It does allow a wide range of values to be fitted on to one graph but more importantly the resolution with which a value such as 1·5 can be located is the same as that for 150. A linear graph cannot do that.

Decibels are a logarithmic ratio. The definition is:

$$dB \text{ value} = 10 \, Log_{10} \left(\frac{Power \ out}{Power \ in} \right)$$

This can be found on most scientific calculators, but seldom is there a need. Doubling the power is +3dB, a further doubling, four times overall, is another 3dB making 6dB in total. Yet another doubling, eight times, makes 9dB. The other value to remember is 10 times is 10dB. By the same logic, a further 10 times is another 10dB or 20dB in total.

The table below shows some common values and their derivation.

dB	Derivation	Linear
3		2×
6	3+3	2×2×=4×
9	3+3+3	2×2×2×=8×
10		10×
20	10+10	10×10×=100×
30	10+10+10	10×10×10×=1000×
13	10+3	10×2×=20×
16	10+3+3	10×2×2×=40×
17	10+10-3	10×10×2÷=50×
14	10+ 10-3-3	10×10×2÷2÷=25

Negative values indicate division. An answer of -6dB indicates the output is a quarter of the input.

The merit of the dB is that the various dB values can be added rather than multiplied.

Alternating Currents and Voltages

The AC waveform was shown in Fig 3.5. Normally the amplitude is given as the RMS value. This is the voltage of a DC supply to a resistive circuit that would have the same heating effect. The peak value (for a sinusoidal waveform) is √2 times larger.

Two AC signals of the same frequency are in phase if they start a new cycle at exactly the same time. The waveforms of current and voltage across a resistor will be in phase. This is not true of many other components. A phase difference between two waveforms is normally expressed in degrees, where 360° is a complete cycle.

A harmonic of an AC signal is another signal of exactly an integer multiple of the frequency. It may not be in phase, but the phase relationship is preserved. Adding harmonics to a signal will change its waveform. It is important to recognise that not only does adding harmonics change the waveform, but that any distortion of a clean sine wave will produce harmonics that were not originally present. If those harmonics can be filtered out (not always possible) then the distortion can be removed.

Capacitors and Inductors

As current flows into a capacitor it charges up and the voltage rises. With a DC supply and a limiting resistor R the time to become charged to about 2/3 of the final value is the Time Constant. The Time Constant is found as C×R seconds, taking care to express C in Farads and R in Ohms. *This is a logarithmic process and the 2/3 value is strictly 1/ε where ε is the base of natural logarithms.*

With an AC supply the effect is that the voltage waveform lags the capacitor charging current waveform by 90°.

The ratio V_{rms}/I_{rms} for a capacitor or inductor is its reactance. Reactance is frequency dependent as well as depending on the capacitance or inductance of the component. The formulas are:

$$X_C = \frac{1}{2\pi f C} \text{ or } X_L = 2\pi f L$$

where f is the frequency in Hz, C is in Farads and L in Henries. The reactance X is in ohms.

Similar rules apply to an inductor but now the current lags the applied voltage by 90°.

To remember which is which, use the word CIVIL. For a capacitor C, the current I is before the voltage V, for an inductor L the voltage comes first.

R and C or R and L in series and parallel

Adding the voltages in a series circuit must now take account of the relative phases of the voltages across R and C or L. They cannot simply be added but require *vector addition*. This is shown in **Fig 3.16**. Since V_R and V_C are at 90° the length of the V_{Supply} vector is given by:

$$V_{Supply} = \sqrt{V_R{}^2 + V_C{}^2}$$

For a parallel circuit it is the currents which are at 90° and they require vector addition in exactly the same way as the voltages.

Resonance

The voltages across a capacitor and inductor in series represent a special case. The voltage across the capacitor will lag the current by 90° and that across the inductor will lead by 90°. They will be 180° apart or in exact anti-phase. In effect they subtract rather than add.

Referring back to the formula above for X_C and X_L shows that are both frequency dependent and will be numerically equal when:

$$2\pi f L = \frac{1}{2\pi f C} \text{ or } f = \frac{1}{2\pi \sqrt{LC}}$$

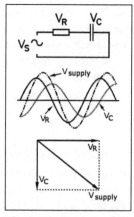

Fig 3.16. Vector addition allows for the addition of voltages of differing phase.

At this frequency the magnitudes of the voltage across C and L will be equal and opposite, giving a vector addition of zero. There is no net voltage across a (perfect) series circuit of L and C and its impedance falls to zero. This condition is known as resonance.

In practice, there will be a small voltage across the resistance of the components, mostly the resistance of the coil.

For the parallel case, the currents in L and C will be equal and opposite, leaving no current in the supply arm. The impedance is infinite, but in the real case the resistance of the coil will result in a small mismatch of currents, giving a very high impedance but not an infinite one. This is shown in **Fig 3.17**.

In series resonance the actual small voltage across the overall circuit can be regarded as being across the small series resistance. The voltage across L and C will be Q times larger where Q is the Q-factor or magnification-factor of the circuit. The quantity Q can be related to the exact shape of the resonance curve and also to the component values.

The same situation applies to parallel resonance but the magnification-factor is now the ratio of the external supply current to the current circulating round the loop of L and C.

In terms of circuit component values:

$$Q = \frac{2\pi f L}{r} = \frac{1}{2\pi f C r}$$

where 'r' is the value of the series resistance, usually of the

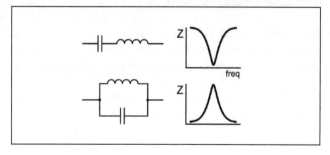

Fig 3.17. Series and parallel LC circuits at resonance.

coil. Note that the resistance at higher frequencies is greater than the DC resistance since the current tends increasingly to flow only in the outer surface of the wire.

In terms of the shape of the resonance curve, the Q-factor is given by:

$$Q = \frac{f_r}{f_h - f_l} = \frac{\text{resonant frequency}}{\text{bandwidth}}$$

This is shown in **Fig 3.18**. The bandwidth, f_h-f_l is measured at the point where the amplitude response (voltage) is 70% ($1/\sqrt{2}$) of the peak. That corresponds to half the power.

At resonance a parallel tuned circuit has a high impedance, in fact it behaves like a resistor of value:

$$R_D = \frac{L}{C\,r}$$

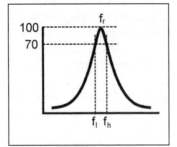

Fig 3.18. The Q-factor determines the sharpness of the resonant curve

where L is in henries, C in farads and r is the series resistance of the coil. R_D is the dynamic resistance or dynamic impedance of the parallel tuned circuit at resonance.

Transformers

The transformer was shown in Fig 3.8. At Advanced you also need to know the various formula for calculating voltage, current and impedance:

$$V_{out} = V_{in} \times \frac{N_S}{N_P} \qquad I_{in} = I_{out} \times \frac{N_S}{N_P} \qquad Z_{in} = Z_{out} \times \left(\frac{N_P}{N_S}\right)^2$$

where N_P is the number of primary turns, N_S the number of secondary turns, Z_{in} is the impedance looking into the primary and Z_{out} is the external load connected to the secondary. Take care to note the use of in / out and primary / secondary.

Filters

The circuits and response curves of the filters are shown in **Fig 3.19**. The corner or cut-off frequency is the half-power point at which $X_C = R$.

The band pass and band stop filters are shown with two sections, either section could be used, but it should be noted that all filters assume correct matching to the source and load impedances (not shown). These types of filter are often quoted in terms of the bandwidths at 6dB and 60dB and the band stop filter as the depth of the 'notch'.

Screening and temperature

Screening prevents unwanted radiation or pickup. Sensitive input circuits may be screened, as should oscillators. Inputs and outputs, including power rails may need filtering.

All components change value slightly as the temperature changes. A positive temperature coefficient indicates an increase in value. 5ppm per degree indicates the value will be 5 parts in a million greater for each 1°C rise. A 10MHz crystal will be 250Hz off-tune for a 5° rise.

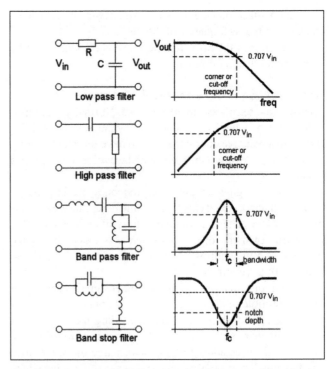

Fig 3.19. Low pass, high pass, band pass and band stop filters.

Semiconductors

N-type material is doped with an element having five electrons in its outer shell, so that there are free electrons in the crystal lattice structure available to conduct electricity. P-type indicates doping with a 3-electon element causing a deficiency of electrons or 'holes'.

In a P-N junction, making the N region positive with an external supply will cause the electrons and holes to move away from the junction and widen the depletion layer. Making the P region positive will narrow the depletion layer and about 0·6V (for silicon) will reduce the layer to zero allowing the onset of conduction. The diode is normally a P-N junction device but there are other constructions for special purposes.

Fig 3.10 showed a half-wave supply charging a capacitor to smooth out the pulses to a reasonably constant DC. On the negative half cycles the peak voltage from the transformer adds to that on the capacitor to reverse bias the diode to twice the peak secondary voltage. Suitable diodes are readily obtained but it is a matter easily overlooked.

For a more constant supply, full wave rectification, shown in **Fig 3.20**, provides twice as many recharge cycles, making smoothing easier and there is also an electronic voltage stabiliser. The input to the stabiliser needs to be sufficient to leave a volt or two across the series pass transistor and the bottom of the input ripple.

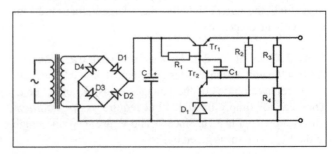

Fig 3.20. A full wave rectifier and stabilised PSU.

The single diode in Fig 3.20 is a Zener diode. It is used reverse biased and is designed to conduct at a set voltage, providing a stable reference. It is non-destructive, provided the current is limited to a safe value.

Transistors

The bipolar junction transistor is a three-layer device, either PNP or NPN (the most common). The base emitter junction is forward biased. This allows the charge carriers, the electrons (for an NPN device) to reach the base emitter boundary. The collector is reverse biased. This prevents the p region 'holes' from crossing the base into the collector, however now, there are electrons just into the base from the emitter. These are swept across the very thin base region into the collector region by the positive voltage on the collector. This could only happen if these electrons were present in the base, at the base emitter boundary, if the base emitter junction is forward biased. A few electrons, fewer than 1% in a small signal transistor, do exit the base at the base connection. That is necessary to maintain the forward biasing on the base emitter junction. This small base current controls the larger collector current and is the basis of current amplification inside the transistor.

The field effect transistor (FET) is quite different in operation. There is a single path or channel from source to drain inside an FET, normally n-type but p-type is available. This channel is surrounded by the opposite type material, the gate, such that the depletion layer (as in a diode) narrows the channel. Increasing reverse bias further narrows and eventually constricts or pinches-off the channel. This controls the source-drain current. Most FETs are n-channel depletion mode type. Depletion mode means that in the absence of additional reverse bias to the gate, the FET will conduct. Enhancement mode means that the channel is so narrow as to be pinched-off without gate bias and a positive voltage on the gate (assuming n-channel) is required to allow conduction.

Transistor amplifier

Fig 3.21 shows the same audio transistor amplifier from Fig 3.12, but now with component values and voltages. A standing current of 500µA has been chosen since the requirement in this example is a low power signal amplifier.

The choice of emitter resistor is down to the designer but is used to provide a more stable bias. The emitter capacitor removes any signal voltages from the emitter that would occur as the collector and emitter current varied. That voltage would tend to reduce the

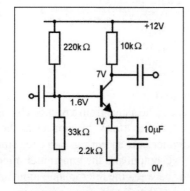

Fig 3.21. A transistor amplifier showing component values and circuit voltages.

signal across the base-emitter junction and reduce the amplification or gain of the circuit. The capacitor needs a low reactance at the lowest frequency of operation. 'Low' in this context is low in comparison to the 2·2kΩ emitter resistor. 10µF is ample.

The collector voltage has been set at 7V, allowing a swing

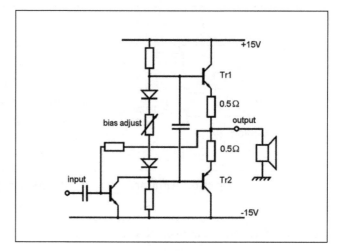

Fig 3.22. A push-pull amplifier.

up to (almost) 12V and down to 2V, which will leave about 1V minimum across the transistor. The potential divider in the base has been chosen to have a standing current of just below 10% of the collector current.

The amplifier is operating in Class-A. That is collector current is flowing throughout the cycle of signal. This is required to avoid distortion of the signal.

Fig 3.22 shows a push-pull amplifier. Here each output transistor can amplify half of the cycle allowing the standing current to be considerably reduced. If it were reduced to almost zero it would be Class-B biasing. In reality, to provide a smoother transition from one transistor to the other and avoid crossover distortion, a small current flows and is strictly class AB biasing.

Fig 3.23 shows the various bias classes and the proportions of a cycle of signal over which collector current is flowing. Classes AB and B require push-pull design to avoid distortion and can be used at both audio and RF. Class C cannot avoid distortion and the distortion products, chiefly harmonics of the signal, must be filtered out. Consequently the technique is only relevant for RF. It is much more efficient at converting DC power to RF and requires less heat sinking. This is especially useful on battery powered and miniaturised

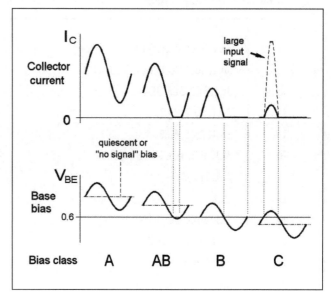

Fig 3.23. The classes of bias and proportion of a cycle for which collector current flows.

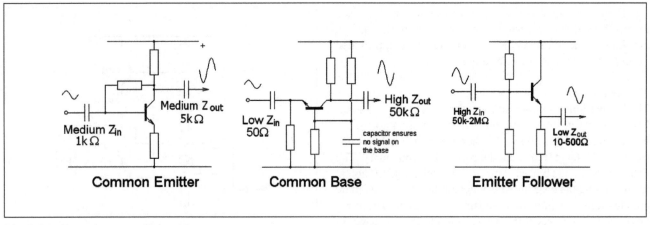

Fig 3.24. Transistor configurations.

equipments.

The transistor can be used in three different configurations. The common one, seen so far, is called the Common Emitter configuration since the emitter is common to both the input and output signal paths. In Common Base, the base is normally connected, at signal frequencies only, to the 0V rail. It cannot be actually connected to 0V (unless both positive and negative power supplies are used) since the DC conditions must be maintained. This configuration has a low input impedance and high output impedance but has the advantage of working at higher frequencies for a given type of transistor. The third configuration is Common Collector; much better known as an Emitter Follower. The emitter follower has a high input impedance and low output impedance. This is often used as a buffer stage to isolate a sensitive circuit such as an oscillator from the circuitry that follows. All three configurations are shown in **Fig 3.24**.

Sample questions

There are 12 questions in the Advanced examination on technical basics distributed round the syllabus items as shown in the table.

Question	Syllabus Item
11	3a.1, 3b.1, 3c.1, 3d.1
12	3e.1, 3e.2, 3e.3, 3e.4, 3e.5
13	3f.1, 3f.2, 3f.3, 3f.4
14	3g.1, 3g.2, 3g.3
15	3h.1, 3h.2, 3h.3
16	3i.1, 3i.2, 3i.3, 3i.4, 3i.5, 3i.6
17	3j.1, 3j.2, 3j.3
18	3k.1
19	3l.1, 3m.1, 3o!
20	3n.1, 3n.2, 3n.3, 3n.4
21	3n.5, 3n.6, 3n.7, 3n.8
22	3p.1, 3p.2, 3p.3

a3a1-1

An antenna is connected by a short feeder to the input to a radio receiver. Everything is correctly matched to 50Ω and a sensitive high impedance RF voltmeter across the feeder records an input to the receiver of 10μV. The receiver is disconnected and the level of RF signal noted. The reading will be about

A   5μV

B   10μV

C   14μV

D   20μV.

a3b1-1

Two resistors are connected in parallel, 20kΩ and 30kΩ. They are then connected in series with an 8kΩ resistor. The effective resistance of the combination is

A   12kΩ

B   20kΩ

C   28kΩ

D   33kΩ.

a3c1-1

A radio receiver is reading S9 on its scale, which the handbook says is an input signal of 50μV PD rms. In 50Ω this represents an input power of

A   0·05pW

B   50pW

C   1nW

D   50μW.

a3d1-1

The audio signal from a packet TNC is 100mV and this must be reduced to 10mV to connect to the transmitter. A potential divider is used with a 10kΩ resistor connected between the TNC output and the transmitter microphone input. The resistor between the microphone input and earth should be

A   900Ω

B   1·0kΩ

C   1·1kΩ

D   10kΩ.

a3e1-1

A trimmer capacitor consists of five foils connected to the body of the device and four foils loosely interleaved between them with a thin insulation to prevent contact. It is adjusted so the spacing is, on average, halved. The capacitance will

A   halve
B   reduce to about 70%
C   increase by about 40%
D   double.

a3e2-1

Apart from the capacitance, another parameter to be considered when selecting a low value capacitor (say 0·1µF) is

A   power handling
B   polarity
C   breakdown voltage
D   internal resistance.

a3e3-1

Capacitors are available with assorted dielectrics, polythene, ceramic etc. A factor affecting the choice of dielectric is

A   linearity
B   leakage resistance
C   phase angle
D   operating frequency.

a3e4-1

A valve receiver has a power supply producing 300V. It takes about 10 seconds to unscrew the lid and it is considered safe if the voltage has dropped to about 100V by the time the lid is off. The smoothing capacitor is 200µF. Approximately what value should be chosen for the bleeder resistor to minimise wasted power?

A   20kΩ.
B   50kΩ.
C   100kΩ.
D   200kΩ.

a3e5-1

The drawing shows a variable capacitor with a preset trimmer at 10pF and a series capacitor. Its purpose is to adjust the overall capacitance to set the tuning range to the desired value. The capacitance of the circuit will vary over the range

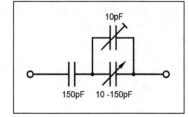

A   9 - 160pF
B   10 - 150pF
C   18 - 78pF
D   18 - 300pF.

a3f1-1

The drawing shows a current flowing through a coil, the arrow shows its direction and the legend, whether the current is increasing, decreasing or remains steady. The '+' symbol shows which end of the coil is positive for the induced back EMF in the coil. Which one correctly shows the polarity of the induced EMF?

A   Drawing A.
B   Drawing B.
C   Drawing C.
D   Drawing D.

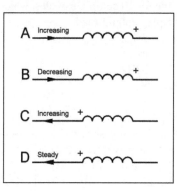

a3f2-1

A coil for use in the IF of a receiver is wound on a hollow former. To adjust the tuning a slug may be screwed into the former core. This slug is normally made of a

A   high permeability material such as ferrite
B   high permittivity material such as ceramic
C   low conductivity material such as tantalum
D   piezoelectric material such as quartz.

a3f3-1

The graph shows the flow of current through a circuit from 'switch on'. The circuit comprises a resistor and

A   capacitor in series
B   inductor in series
C   capacitor in parallel
D   inductor in parallel.

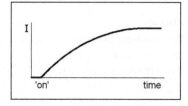

a3f4-1

An antenna matching unit (AMU or ATU) has switched inductors connected in series. L1 and L2 are each 20µH and L3 is 50µH. The three inductors are well spaced apart to avoid unwanted interaction. The maximum inductance is

A   12µH
B   40µH
C   50µH
D   90µH.

a3g1-1

An 50Hz AC signal of 10V peak is applied to a resistor and the temperature rise noted. What voltage of a DC supply will result in the same temperature?

A   5V.
B   7V.
C   10V.
D   14V.

a3g2-1
A low frequency signal is applied to a frequency meter. For measuring low frequencies the meter actually measures the time for 10 complete cycles, which is 800mS. The frequency display should read
A   1·25Hz
B   8Hz
C   12·5Hz
D   80Hz.

a3g3-1
The drawing shows the voltage waveforms in a circuit fed with an AC signal. Waveform B (shown dashed) LAGS waveform A by
A   90°
B   180°
C   270°
D   360°.

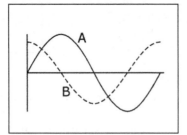

a3h1-1
A 318pF capacitor has a reactance at 1MHz of
A   500Ω
B   1000Ω
C   1570Ω
D   5000Ω.

a3h1-2
The drawing shows the current and voltage waveforms in an unknown component. The component is probably a
A   resistor
B   capacitor
C   inductor
D   diode.

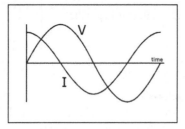

a3h2-1
A resistor of 400Ω and a capacitor of 0·1μF are fed from an AC source. At a certain frequency the reactance of the capacitor is 300Ω. The impedance of the circuit is
A   300Ω
B   400Ω
C   500Ω
D   700Ω.

a3h3-1
A transistor amplifier is shown in the circuit diagram. Capacitor C3 is used for
A   coupling
B   decoupling
C   buffering
D   blocking.

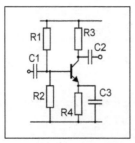

a3i1-1
At 10MHz a long wire antenna presents a capacitive reactance at its feed point equivalent to a capacitor of 20pF. What inductance is required to bring the system to resonance?
A   12·5μH.
B   25μH.
C   40μH.
D   80μH.

a3i2-1
The graph shows the response of a
A   series resonant circuit
B   parallel resonant circuit
C   mains filter
D   low pass filter.

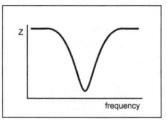

a3i3-1
A series resonant circuit has 10V peak across it when at resonance. At that frequency the resistance of the coil is approximately 4Ω and the Q-factor is calculated as 100. The voltage across the capacitor will be about
A   40V
B   100V
C   400V
D   1000V.

a3i3-2
A 3·5MHz tuned circuit has a 3dB bandwidth of 35kHz. At that frequency the reactance of both the coil and capacitor are calculated to be 2·4kΩ. The coil resistance will be about
A   2·4Ω
B   3·5Ω
C   24Ω
D   35Ω.

a3i4-1
What is the impedance at resonance of a parallel tuned circuit comprising a capacitor of 32pF and a coil of 32μH having an internal resistance of 25Ω?
A   800Ω.
B   25·6kΩ.
C   40kΩ.
D   125kΩ.

a3i5-1
Which drawing shows the equivalent circuit of a crystal?
A   Drawing A.
B   Drawing B.
C   Drawing C.
D   Drawing D.

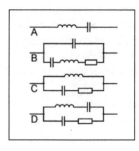

a3i6-1

Some antenna matching units can have tuned circuits with a high Q-factor. A significant implication of this is that

A there will be a need to reduce the Q-factor for satisfactory reception of wide band signals

B the circulating currents and voltages in the tuned circuits can be very high

C tuning the receiver to the wanted signal can become quite critical

D a low pass filter is also desirable to limit harmonic radiation.

a3j1-1

In a transformer the energy is transferred from the primary to the secondary by

A mutual inductance

B electromagnetic coupling

C magnetic resonance

D eddy current conduction.

a3j2-1

A valve RF amplifier requires a load impedance of 1.8kΩ which needs to be matched to a 50Ω output. The secondary has 5 turns, how many turns are required on the primary?

A 30.

B 36.

C 180.

D 250.

a3j3-1

The core of power transformers is laminated in order to

A enhance the magnetic field

B improve the coupling from primary to secondary

C minimise the effect of eddy currents

D reduce to risk of vibration and 'hum'.

a3k1-1

The low pass filter shown in the diagram has a cut-off frequency of

A 30kHz

B 35kHz

C 40kHz

D 50kHz.

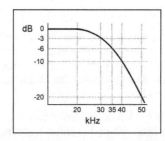

a3l1-1

Unwanted radiation from a local oscillator stage in a receiver can be minimised by using

A a balanced output form the oscillator

B an emitter follower buffer stage

C a thin metal cover round the oscillator

D bipolar transistors in preference to FETs.

a3m1-1

The coil in the LC tuned circuit normally increases its inductance as the temperature rises. One solution to minimise frequency drift is to

A use a capacitor with a negative temperature coefficient

B use a capacitor with a positive temperature coefficient

C mount the capacitor further away from any source of heat

D mount the coil vertically to minimise the temperature gradient.

a3n1-1

The 'P' type semiconductor is doped with an element containing

A more electrons in the outer shell than are required for bonding

B fewer electrons in the outer shell than are required for bonding

C positively charged ions to improve the conductivity of pure silicon

D small amounts of copper to change the silicon to a semi-conductor.

a3n2-1

A Zener diode is

A forward biased to provide a specified reference voltage

B reverse biased to provide a specified reference voltage

C forward biased to provide an accurately known current

D reverse biased to prevent excessive current flow.

a3n3-1

The dielectric in a varicap diode is formed from the

A potential barrier at the p-n junction when forward biased

B small region of un-doped silicon produced in manufacture

C depletion layer of a reverse biased diode

D electron-hole pairs in the junction region.

a3n4-1

The path from source to drain inside an FET comprises

A a continuous path entirely of N-type (or P-type) material

B a single P-N junction which is normally forward biased

C a single P-N junction which is normally reverse biased

D two junctions, one forward and the other reverse biased.

a3n5-1

The drawing shows a class A amplifier using an N-channel depletion mode FET. The source and drain voltages are shown. What voltage might be expected on the gate in normal operation.

A 3·2V

B 5·2V

C 9·2V

D 16V.

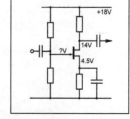

a3n6-1

A transistor amplifier has a current gain of one and a voltage gain of about 30. It is likely that the configuration of the device is

A emitter follower

B common emitter

C common base

D common collector.

a3n7-1

An amplifier operated in class C is particularly suited to

A audio and low frequency signals

B a push-pull output stage for audio or RF

C radio frequencies for AM and SSB

D radio frequencies for CW and FM.

a3n8-1

A power amplifier, run at 13·6V, is rated to give 50W output on FM. A suitable power supply should be rated at no less than

A   5A

B   8A

C   12A

D   20A.

a3o1-1

A pre-amplifier, having 50Ω input and output impedances, is specified as giving 40μV out for 10μV in. Its gain, in dB, is

A   6dB

B   10dB

C   12dB

D   30dB.

a3p1-1

Different types of rectifier circuit may have different smoothing capacitor requirements for the same degree of ripple on the output when on-load. Which of the three types shown have the same requirement?

      1) half-wave

      2) centre-tapped transformer

      3) bridge

A   1 and 2 are the same.

B   1 and 3 are the same.

C   2 and 3 are the same.

D   All of these are the same.

a3p2-1

The secondary of a power supply transformer for a valve receiver produces 200V rms. A half-wave rectifier is used feeding a smoothing capacitor. The maximum reverse voltage across the diode will be about

A   200V

B   300V

C   400V

D   600V.

a3p3-1

The circuit diagram shows a regulated supply for 13·6V. The voltage across the Zener diode D will be about

A   0·7V

B   3V

C   6V

D   10V.

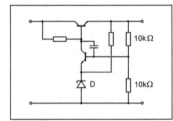

4. Transmitters and Receivers

The block diagram of a transmitter is shown in **Fig 4.1**. The weak audio signal from the microphone is amplified in block 1 and passed to the modulator. The radio frequency generator or oscillator, block 3, produces the radio frequency carrier which sets the transmit frequency. It must be stable, that is it must not drift off frequency and the frequency display must be accurate to ensure operation inside the amateur bands.

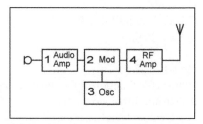

Fig 4.1. Transmitter block diagram.

Block 2 is the modulator. The modulator places the audio signal on the carrier. In amplitude modulation (AM), the amplitude (height) of the carrier is varied in exact time with the audio. In frequency modulation (FM) it is the precise frequency that varies in exact time with the carrier. This is shown in **Fig 4.2**.

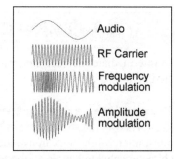

Fig 4.2. Modulation places the audio signal on the RF carrier.

The RF amplifier in block 4 takes the output from the modulator and amplifies it to a level suitable for transmission. It is then passed to the feeder and antenna where it is radiated.

A data signal could be fed to the modulator as set audio tones from a modem or computer sound card. It is also possible to transmit SSB, single sideband. This is not shown in Fig 4.2, but is a type of AM. That is covered in the Intermediate examination.

The correct feeder and antenna must be used for the transmitter so it provides the correct load on the transmitter. The wrong load is a bit like using the wrong gear on a bicycle or car. It won't work properly and may even be damaged. Using the right load is called 'correct matching'.

If the audio signal were stronger than shown in Fig 4.2, then the variation in amplitude or frequency of the modulated RF would be greater. It would sound rough and distorted at the receiver, but the real sin is that your transmission may cause interference to those on nearby frequencies. Correctly setting the microphone gain should avoid this but beware

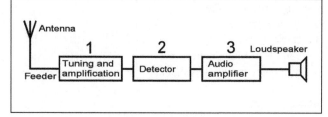

Fig 4.3. Receiver block diagram.

that a desk microphone or modem may have a different output and require different settings.

Fig 4.3 shows a simple block diagram of a receiver. The antenna will pick up many signals, all quite weak, so the first task in to select the wanted signal and amplify it. That is the receiver must be tuned to the correct signal. That is performed in box 1. We now have just one modulated signal, which has also been amplified. It is passed to the demodulator (or detector) where the original modulating signal is recovered. Finally the audio amplifier makes this signal strong enough for headphones or a loudspeaker. For data, the output would be fed to the modem or PC sound card.

Sample Questions

The specification shows that three questions will be asked.

Question	Syllabus Item
11	4a.1, 4b.1, 4b.2, 4b.3
12	4b.4, 4b.5, 4b.6
13	4c.1, 4d.1, 4d.2

f4a1-1

Which two blocks in a transmitter feed signals IN to the modulator?

A   RF amplifier and feeder.
B   Microphone amplifier and oscillator.
C   Oscillator and RF amplifier.
D   Microphone amplifier and RF amplifier.

f4b1-1

Which stage of a transmitter will, if set wrongly, result in transmission on the wrong frequency?

A   Microphone amplifier.
B   Modulator.
C   RF amplifier.
D   Oscillator.

f4b2-1

Which is the FIRST point in a transmitter that an AM signal could be found?

A From the RF amplifier.
B From the modulator.
C From the microphone amplifier.
D From the oscillator.

f4b3-1

The signal marked 'X' in the drawing represents the

A audio signal
B carrier signal
C amplitude modulated signal
D frequency modulated signal.

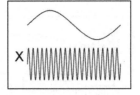

f4b4-1

Which stage in the radio transmitter feeds the signal to the antenna?

A Oscillator.
B Microphone Amplifier.
C RF Amplifier.
D Modulator.

f4b5-1

Connecting a transmitter to the wrong antenna may mean

A poor modulation
B damage to the RF power amplifier
C very low SWR on the feeder
D transmitting off-frequency.

f4b6-1

Interference caused to other stations on frequencies above and below the one you are using might be caused by

A setting the transmitter to the wrong frequency
B over-modulation, due to setting the microphone gain too high
C setting the output power too far below the licence limit
D speaking for far too long on a single over.

f4c1-1

The diagram shows the different blocks of a radio receiver disconnected and arranged in the wrong order. The input of each block is at the left hand end and the output is on the right. Which connection below is correct?

A Point 2 to point 3.
B Point 3 to point 8.
C Point 4 to point 5.
D Point 6 to point 3.

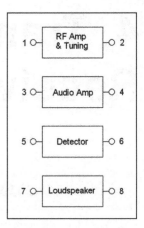

f4d1-1

A function carried out in the first stage of a radio receiver is

A detection
B tuning
C audio amplification
D oscillating.

f4d2-1

What is the function of the stage in a radio receiver following the RF amplifier and tuning?

A Demodulator (detector).
B Audio amplifier.
C Loudspeaker or headphones.
D Oscillator.

INTERMEDIATE

At Intermediate level the transmitter and receiver are considered in more depth.

Transmitter architecture

Fig 4.4 shows the architecture of the four main types of radio transmitter. Multi-mode transmitters will have a combined architecture able to handle all the functions.

The microphone amplifier increases the audio signal level and has a filter to limit the audio frequency range to around 3kHz. It may also have an amplitude limiter to provide some protection against over-modulation.

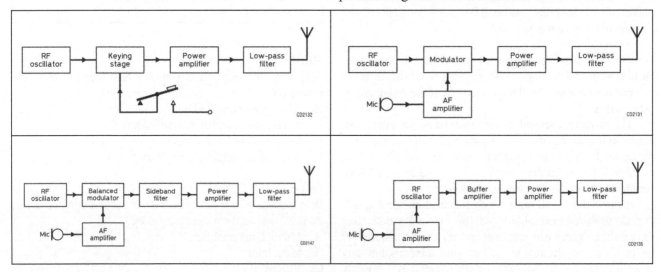

Fig 4.4. The block diagrams of CW, AM SSB and FM transmitters.

The oscillator is often run from a separate supply line to avoid heavy currents drawn by the power amplifier having unwanted effects. The oscillator is also of sturdy construction, located away from sources of heat and screened to prevent pickup. The crystal oscillator is very stable but cannot be varied in frequency. The LC tuned circuit oscillator can be varied but lacks stability. For this reason a crystal controlled synthesiser is often employed allowing a variable frequency (in small steps) with the accuracy and stability of a crystal.

Modulation

Four types of modulation are considered.

CW (carrier wave) or Morse simply keys the signal from the oscillator. The oscillator runs continuously to ensure stability and the keying is normally in a buffer stage following the oscillator so the oscillator is unaffected by the keying. Morse is very effective, achieving considerable range with minimum power and bandwidth.

AM was shown in Fig 4.2. When a carrier is modulated, it takes up more room in the radio frequency spectrum. This is shown in **Fig 4.5**. The amplitude modulator is a special case of a mixer, a device commonly used in both transmitters and receivers. The band-width of an AM signal is twice that of the audio signal. To allow more users to share the band and to avoid interference to adjacent channel users, the audio bandwidth is limited in the microphone amplifier. The amplitude limiter prevents over-modulation, which will also cause adjacent channel (adjacent in frequency) interference.

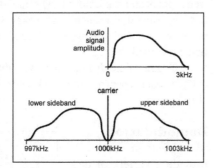

Fig 4.5. The spectrum of an AM signal.

Fig 4.6 shows a mixer. Input f1 will be an audio signal comprising all frequencies from about 300Hz to 3kHz. The carrier frequency, f2, comes from the oscillator. The output f1+f2 will be a range of frequencies starting 300Hz above the carrier up to 3kHz above the carrier. It will appear as if all the audio frequencies have been shifted up in frequency to sit just above the carrier. This forms the upper sideband in Fig 4.5. Similarly, the output

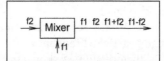

Fig 4.6. A mixer combines or mixes two signals to produce outputs at several frequencies.

f1-f2 will form a lower sideband extending from 300Hz below the carrier frequency down to 3kHz below the carrier.

An SSB transmitter uses a balanced mixer. The inputs f1 and f2, the carrier, are not present in its output, only the sum and difference frequencies, which are the upper and lower sidebands. Since f1+f2 is a carbon copy of the audio, just shifted up in frequency, all the voice information is contained in that sideband. The same is true of f1-f2, the lower sideband, but the frequencies are inverted; a higher audio frequency causes a lower RF signal.

The sidebands are RF, they will radiate just as well as the carrier. We can dispense with the carrier and either one of the

sidebands. This saves half the transmitted bandwidth and the power in the carrier and the other sideband. The system is much more efficient and will have a greater range for the same overall transmit power.

Frequency Modulation is applied at the RF oscillator. The frequency of oscillation is controlled by an LC tuned circuit and the C is partly formed by a variable capacitance diode. Feeding audio to the reverse biased diode will vary the capacitance, which will vary the frequency of oscillation. The bandwidth depends on the amount by which the frequency is changed during modulation, but it does require the greatest bandwidth of the modes discussed.

Feeding audio data tones into the microphone is possible with any modulation mode. Packet, for example uses two 'tones' and uses FM on the VHF and UHF bands. Other systems are used on HF and typically use two or more tones. The more complex systems can provide good immunity from interference, which is common on HF.

Power Amplifier

The power amplifier has now been split into the PA itself and a low pass filter (LPF). The filter removes harmonics of the transmitted signal. Any active device can produce harmonics but mixers and power amplifier are the worst culprits. If not filtered out, the harmonics can cause interference to other amateur bands and other radio users.

A low-pass filter (LPF) allows low frequencies to pass but restricts higher ones. In a transmitter the 'cut-off' frequency will be set just above the intended output so as to pass the transmitted signal but limit harmonics.

A high-pass filter (HPF) attenuates low frequencies but passes higher ones. TV transmissions range from 470-854MHz; an HPF set to around 450MHz will permit the TV signals to pass but block HF and VHF signals. That filter would be fitted at the input of a TV. The 430-440MHz UHF amateur band will be attenuated, but not to the same degree as lower HF and VHF frequencies.

A band pass filter allows just a given band through. That is more common at VHF and above. Frequencies above and below the 'pass-band' are blocked. Similarly a band-stop filter passes everything except a given band. Typically this may be a 'notch-filter' where the aim is to attenuate a narrow range of frequencies around a particular interferer. The frequency/amplitude responses are shown in **Fig 4.7**.

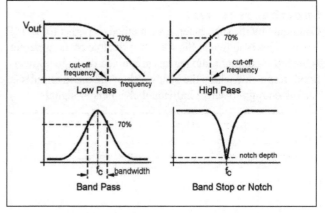

Fig 4.7. Low-pass, high-pass, band-pass and band stop or 'notch' filters. The low and band pass filters will reduce harmonics and the notch will help remove a particular interferer.

The remaining filter we must know is a keying or key-click filter. This is used with a Morse key to smooth the rise and fall of the transmitted signal or 'envelope'. Fast edges are a bit like a too high audio frequency and will dramatically increase the bandwidth. Clicks may be heard several kHz from a badly keyed CW signal. This may occur when the key makes contact, breaks contact or both. The key-click filter prevents this and also avoids sparking at the key contacts in valve operated equipment.

Receivers

The simplest receiver is the crystal set, shown in **Fig 4.8**. The tuned circuit selects the desired frequency and the diode demodulates or detects to audio signal; see demodulation below. Today the bands are crowded and this simple receiver has difficulty selecting only the wanted signal. It also needs a good

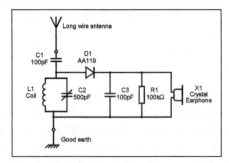

Fig 4.8. A crystal set, the simplest type of radio receiver.

long wire antenna to pick up a sufficiently strong signal to be heard in a earpiece.

Receiver architecture

The architecture of the receiver does not change as much for different modes as it does in the transmitter. Choice of mode only really affects the demodulator stage.

The block diagram considered at Foundation, Fig 4.3, is known as a tuned radio frequency (TRF) receiver. The tuning is carried out at the radio frequency and so is the demodulation. As the radio frequency increases this method suffers from a serious disadvantage. The tuning uses LC tuned circuits. These are able to select a narrow range of frequencies (the bandwidth) down to around 1% of the actual frequency and slightly narrower if several tuned circuits are used. For medium wave AM broadcasts (526-1606kHz) this is fine. At 145MHz the bandwidth would be about 1MHz which is quite useless for selecting the right 12·5 or 25kHz channel.

Superhet receiver

Consequently the superheterodyne method (superhet for short) is used. This is shown in **Fig 4.9**. The principle of the superhet is that all incoming radio signals are mixed down to a lower, fixed, frequency where the bandwidth of the tuned circuits is narrow enough to select individual channels or signals.

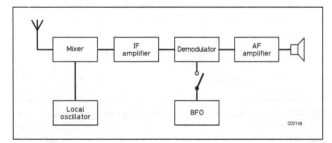

Fig 4.9. A superhet radio receiver.

An RF amplifier is optional. For the amateur HF bands, a switched filter for each band may be employed rather then the continuously variable RF tuning of the TRF design. Broadcast signals are much stronger than amateur signals and some filtering, even without an RF amplifier is often desirable.

The local oscillator (LO) is similar to the oscillator in the transmitter and produces a clean stable frequency.

The mixer combines the signal from the LO and RF amp (or direct from the antenna if there is no RF amp) to produce new frequencies. This was shown in Fig 4.6. There the purpose was to use the mixer as a modulator, here both inputs are at a higher frequency. F1 will be the radio signal, say at 7MHz and f2 the local oscillator at, say, 6·54MHz. The sum frequency will be 13·54MHz and the difference one at 460kHz. The modulation, that is the sidebands on the RF signal f1 will also mix with the LO, f2, so the output will also carry the modulation. The mixer output is band-pass filtered so only f1-f2 gets through. That is termed the intermediate frequency (IF).

The IF amplifier is fix-tuned. It only amplifies a narrow range of frequencies. Tuning the radio is achieved by tuning the LO so that the wanted signal appears at the mixer output at the intermediate frequency. Unwanted signals will be at other frequencies and are ignored. Although the tuning knob controls the oscillator frequency, at 6·54MHz in this example, the tuning dial or digital display will read 7MHz, the frequency being received.

The gain of the IF amplifier is variable so the demodulator can feed back a control signal to keep the signal levels reasonably constant.

Demodulation

Most amateur receivers provide a variety of demodulators. AM is recovered with a diode detector as shown in **Fig 4.10**. The negative part of the modulated IF signal is removed by the diode and a small capacitor will smooth out the RF ripple but retain the audio signal.

CW is recovered using a Beat Frequency

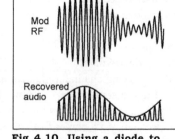

Fig 4.10. Using a diode to remove the negative portion of the modulated IF allows recovery of the audio.

Oscillator (BFO) as shown in Fig 4.9. If the IF is at 460kHz, then setting the BFO to 459·3 or 460·7kHz will result in a beat note of 700Hz when the IF signal is present. That is the Morse signal.

Recovery of an SSB signal is very similar. The BFO, now called a CIO, carrier insertion oscillator is set to 460kHz. An audio upper sideband signal on the IF at 461·4kHz will beat or mix with the 460kHz CIO, to produce an audio note of 1400Hz, all the other audio notes in the signal are recovered in the same way. The demodulator is called a 'product detector' when used in this manner.

Finally, a different circuit called a frequency discriminator is required for FM. The circuit is discussed in the Advanced course.

For AM, CW and SSB an output from the detector/ demodulator is needed that is proportional to the signal strength. That is used to feed the AGC, automatic gain control, to adjust the IF gain to keep the levels reasonably constant. Since FM only uses the instantaneous frequency and is independent of amplitude, no AGC is needed and the IF operates at maximum gain all the time.

The final block in the receiver is the audio amplifier. There are no new issues to cover at Intermediate level.

Sample Questions

Seven questions are asked on transmitters and receivers.

Question	Syllabus Item
18	4a.1 4a.2 4b.1 4b.2 4b.3 4b.4 4c.1
19	4d.1 4d.2 4d.3 4d.4 4d.5
20	4e.1 4e.2
21	4e.3 4e.4
22	4f.1 4f.2
23	4g.1 4h.1
24	4i.1 4i.2 4j.1

i4a1-1

What mode of transmission requires the architecture of transmitter shown?
A   Amplitude modulation.
B   Single sideband.
C   Frequency modulation.
D   Morse - CW.

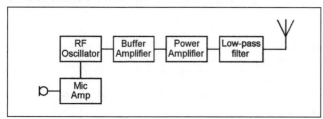

i4a2-1

The drawing shows the block diagram of a transmitter. What is the function of the box marked 'X'?
A   Sideband filter.
B   Harmonic filter.
C   High-pass filter.
D   Low pass filter.

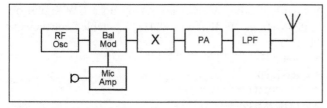

i4b1-1

When considering whether to use a crystal oscillator or a VFO in a home-made transmitter, an amateur should note that a
A   crystal will give a readily tuneable frequency of high accuracy
B   VFO makes it easy to change frequency but may lack stability
C   VFO gives a more stable frequency that a crystal oscillator
D   crystal can only be tuned in fixed steps, determined on manufacture.

i4b2-1

The output frequency of a variable frequency oscillator depends on the
A   amount of gain of the associated transistor
B   bias setting of the associated transistor
C   calibration of the dial on the transmitter front panel
D   values of L and C in a resonant circuit.

i4b3-1

To help prevent a continuously tuneable transmitter from drifting off frequency it is advisable to
A   run the power amplifier from a specially stabilised supply
B   rigidly construct the VFO and put it in its own screened box
C   mount the oscillator as close as possible to the power amplifier
D   use a band-pass filter immediately after the modulator.

i4b4-1

A key advantage of using a synthesiser as the oscillator in a transmitter is that
A   the frequency can be shown on a digital display
B   it is tuneable and has the frequency stability of a crystal
C   all the different modes of modulation are available in one transmitter
D   the tuning is continuously variable rather than in fixed steps.

i4c1-1

A mixer is fed with a 10·5MHz signal and a signal from a variable frequency oscillator. Outputs are noted on 7MHz and 14MHz. What is the VFO frequency?
A   3·5MHz.
B   7·0MHz.
C   17·5MHz.
D   24·5MHz.

i4d1-1

A signal at 3·5MHz and an audio signal are fed to a mixer. This results in new frequencies called
A   sidebands
B   harmonics
C   side tones
D   bandwidths.

i4d2-1

An amplitude modulated signal consists of
A   a carrier and it harmonics
B   a carrier and a sideband
C   two sidebands but no carrier
D   two sidebands and a carrier.

i4d3-1

In a single sideband transmission the
A   carrier radiates most of the transmitted power
B   bandwidth is about twice the highest audio frequency used
C   carrier is only needed when transmitting
D   bandwidth is half that of amplitude modulation.

i4d4-1
It is noticed that a transmission contains two audio tones, which seem to be sent alternately. The transmission is probably
A using double rather than single sideband
B a type of data signal
C from a very unstable transmitter
D not from an amateur station.

i4d5-1
The device shown by the circuit symbol might be found
A on the front panel of a transmitter to indicate transmission
B in a transmitter power supply
C in an audio amplifier
D in a frequency modulator.

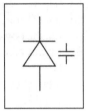

i4e1-1
An amplitude modulated transmission on 14·200MHz is over-modulated. This may cause interference to other stations on
A 14·100MHz
B 14·196MHz
C 28·4MHz
D 42·6MHz.

i4e2-1
An oscillator is set to 3·60MHz. Outputs may also be noted on
A 1·80MHz
B 7·10MHz
C 7·20MHz
D 7·60MHz.

i4e3-1
A harmonic of your transmission is quite likely to be heard by
A other amateurs in the same band
B radio users just above and below your amateur band
C other amateurs in a different amateur band
D the amateur you are in contact with.

i4e4-1
Harmonics of your transmitter can be reduced by using a
A low-pass filter
B high-pass filter
C ferrite ring on your feeder
D balun fitted close to the antenna.

i4e5-1
Which transmitted envelope of a CW signal will result in the minimum occupied bandwidth?
A Envelope A.
B Envelope B.
C Envelope C.
D Envelope D.

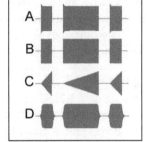

i4f1-1
The block diagram of a radio receiver is shown. What is the function of the box marked 'X'?
A Mixer.
B Demodulator (detector).
C IF amplifier.
D RF amplifier.

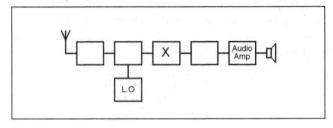

i4f2-1
The stage in a radio receiver which provides the most gain and selectivity is the
A RF amplifier
B local oscillator
C IF amplifier
D audio amplifier.

i4g1-1
A radio receiver is tuned to 7·05MHz and the intermediate frequency is 465kHz. The local oscillator will be on a frequency of
A 462kHz
B 465kHz
C 6585kHz
D 7050kHz.

i4h1-1
The wanted signal is selected from amongst those on many other frequencies by the tuned circuits in
A the RF and IF amplifiers
B only the RF amplifier
C the mixer
D the audio amplifier.

i4i1-1
A superhet radio receiver is picking up a CW signal on 14·020MHz and the IF is on 460kHz. A suitable frequency for the BFO is
A 460·0kHz
B 460·7kHz
C 14·020MHz
D 14·021MHz.

i4i1-2
A superhet radio receiver is picking up an SSB signal on 14·220MHz and the IF is on 460kHz. A suitable frequency for the CIO is
A 460·0kHz
B 460·7kHz
C 14·220MHz
D 14·221MHz.

i4i2-1

Which one of the waveforms shown will be seen at the output of a diode detector for AM?

A   Waveform A.
B   Waveform B.
C   Waveform C.
D   Waveform D.

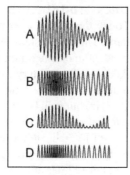

i4j1-1

The signal used to produce the AGC feedback to the IF amplifier is obtained from the

A   RF amplifier
B   AF amplifier
C   local oscillator
D   detector.

ADVANCED

At this level the architecture and circuits inside each of the boxes is considered in some detail. Fig 4.4 showed the basic architecture of transmitters for various modes, but they all assumed that the RF oscillator worked at the transmit frequency and modulation was carried out at that frequency. Often a transmitter will be capable of all the modes and modulation is carried out a lower, fixed, frequency. This is similar to the concept of an IF in a superhet radio receiver. The reason is similar too. It is easier to perform the modulation at a fixed frequency and then mix it up to the final transmit frequency.

Fig 4.11 shows such a transmitter. The crystal oscillator feeding the modulator could run at around 6MHz although designs will vary considerably. The modulator is likely to be multi-mode and its output is mixed with the signal from the frequency synthesiser to produce the transmit frequency. Each modulation and mixing stage needs careful screening and filtering since these processes can generate a whole multitude of spurious signals at different frequencies.

A transceiver combines the transmitter and receiver, allowing many functions to be shared. Certainly the oscillators and IF stages will be common and switching is used to route the signals appropriately for transmit or receive. Nonetheless the following text will treat transmit and receive functions separately.

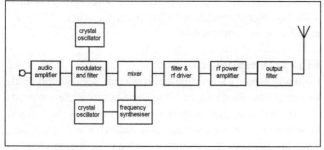

Fig 4.11. A transmitter modulating at a fixed frequency and mixing up to the final frequency.

Oscillators

In this design the modulator will be fed from a fixed frequency crystal oscillator such as shown in **Fig 4.12**. A similar design

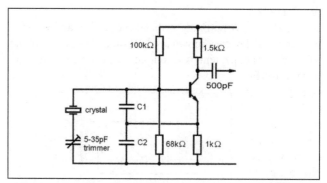

Fig 4.12. A crystal oscillator produces a single fixed frequency.

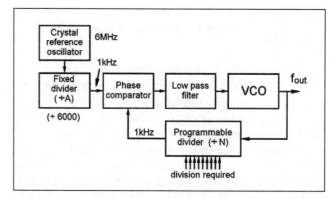

Fig 4.13. A frequency synthesiser based on a phase lock loop, PLL.

will be used to feed the synthesiser.

The synthesiser produces a sine wave in discrete frequency steps by one of two methods. A phase lock loop (PLL) or direct frequency synthesis. A PLL is shown in block diagram form in **Fig 4.13**. The crystal oscillator is digitally divided down to produce a reference frequency, in this case 1kHz. The VCO is a voltage controlled oscillator, a variable frequency oscillator where the frequency is set by an input control voltage. The output is also divided down, but the division ratio is user controlled. If we assume the division is 10,000 and the VCO is running at 10MHz, then that too will produce a 1kHz signal. Both 1kHz signals are fed to the phase comparator and any error used to adjust the VCO. Resetting the variable division to 9,999 will result in the ensuing error from the comparator re-setting the VCO to 9· 999MHz and restoring the 1kHz input to the comparator. The output is now able to be set in 1kHz increments but with crystal accuracy.

One risk in the PLL system is that the VCO will be so far off frequency that the phase comparator output swings wildly causing the VCO to do likewise. Design to achieve a rapid lock is important but an unstable output is so serious that an out-of-lock signal is needed to inhibit transmission until lock is achieved.

Direct frequency synthesis is more recent and required the development of fast digital to analogue conversion. Simplistically the values of a sine wave are stored in a table and played out in much the same manner as the digital signal on a music CD. The frequency is determined by the 'playback' speed. The quality of the sine wave is determined by the number of samples of its amplitude over a cycle and the number of digital bits defining the amplitude at each sample point. Errors in this process form noise and harmonics, which need to be minimised.

Modulator

The modulator is normally of balanced design and a transformer based device is shown in **Fig 4.14**. Being balanced, the RF carrier is not present in the output. The carrier is by far the most powerful signal present and would otherwise be the most difficult to remove. Nonetheless removing the unwanted sideband does call for careful filtering and a crystal filter

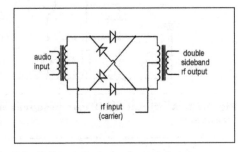

Fig 4.14. A balanced modulator.

may well be used unless the modulation is at a relatively low frequency. Normal amplitude modulation can be achieved by re-inserting the carrier or unbalancing the modulator. The transformer design is not amenable to being unbalanced, but a wholly semiconductor implementation, normally an IC, is.

Frequency modulation is often not performed on the oscillator in order to maintain stability. Instead, the signal is actually phase modulated. Changing the frequency will result in phase changes, the difference between FM and PM lies only in which variable, frequency or phase, is directly related to the instantaneous amplitude of the audio signal. Pre-conditioning the audio in an RC circuit will allow a true phase modulator to produce FM. PM occupies a greater bandwidth but is less susceptible to high frequency noise. In that sense, it is equivalent to the pre-emphasis in FM broadcast transmissions.

AM bandwidth is simply twice the highest audio frequency, comprising both sidebands and the carrier. SSB has the same bandwidth as the audio and comprises a single sideband.

FM has several sidebands, theoretically an infinite number but only those of any magnitude, close to the carrier are of significance. The generally accepted rule, Carson's Rule gives the necessary bandwidth as:

$$\text{Bandwidth} = 2\,(f_A + \Delta f_C)$$

where f_A is the highest audio modulating frequency, and Δf_C is the peak deviation.

This rule tends to over-estimate the bandwidth for narrow band modulation, that is where the modulation index m (m= peak deviation/highest audio frequency), is around or below unity.

An excessive signal into the modulator will cause overmodulation. On FM this may simply be excessive deviation, although that will risk interference to adjacent channels and possibly poor audio reception. On AM the peaks and troughs of the envelope may be clipped, distorting the audio and causing harmonics of the audio, which will exceed the 3kHz bandwidth and splatter into adjacent channels. On SSB and possibly on AM the peaks may overload the PA, again distorting the audio and a small risk of clipping the RF as well. If the latter does occur then there will be harmonics of the RF as well as of the audio.

Data Modulation

Today there is an enormous range of data modulation systems. The new systems were developed to achieve minimum bandwidth or maximum immunity to noise and interference. Additionally military systems used spread spectrum techniques to hide the transmission as a wide-band signal (say 10MHz) but well below the noise floor, even though the data rate was only a few kbits/sec.

RTTY, radio teletype, was an early form of data and is still much in use today. In amateur use RTTY comprises two audio tones of 1275Hz and 1445Hz fed to the transmitter with a data rate of 45·5 or 50 baud. If this is fed to an FM transmitter the ITU emission code is F2B; fed to an SSB transmitter the code is J2B. The other option is to feed the original data signal direct to the modulator so two different RF frequencies are transmitted, 170Hz apart. That would then be emission code F1B. Since a 1275Hz tone sent to an SSB transmitter set to 7000kHz would produce a single RF signal on 7001·275kHz, a J2B and F1B transmission are indistinguishable off-air. Either way, accurate tuning of the receiver is required. The reader should also see comments on data reception in the receiver section.

Speech processing

Speech is very 'peaky', the peak to average ratio is some 13dB or 20:1 in power. The Full licence permits the power to peak at 400W. Without processing that means an average power of 20W! Simple processing just clips the peaks with a diode allowing the average level to be increased. This causes harmonics of the audio frequencies and a rough sound. The harmonics above 3kHz are removed by the filter but lower notes have in-band harmonics so the roughness remains.

If the audio is mixed up to, say, 50 - 53kHz and then clipped, the harmonics are 100 - 106kHz and easily removed. Some small artefacts such as in-band intermodulation remain, but much of the roughness is removed. The signal is then mixed back down to audio.

That description is how external processors work. Internally the speech processing can be done after modulation in the transmit IF. Exactly the same end effect, but no need to mix back down to audio.

Processing reduces the peak to average ratio. The average transmit power is increased by typically 6 to 10dB although 10dB does sound a bit over-done. The PA has to work that much harder and will get a lot hotter as a result. A guide to its real power handling capability is the output power quoted in the equipment specification for AM or FM where the carrier is transmitted continuously.

Linear Amplifiers

Normally linearity in an amplifier is critical. Non-linearity leads to harmonics of a single frequency and intermodulation products (IMPs) if several frequencies are present, as they would be with a voice transmission. Using inductive, ie transformer, coupling between stages helps to minimise harmonics, but intentionally non-linear stages usually need filtering.

In general, any non-linearity will result in additional frequencies given by:

$$F = m \times f_1 + n \times f_2$$

where f_1 and f_2 are the input frequencies and 'm' and 'n' are integers $0, \pm1, \pm2, \pm3$ etc.

With f_3 present at the input as well, the number of possible combinations magnify enormously. The quantity m+n (ignoring any '-' signs) is the *order* of the intermodulation. Odd order products are very close to the input frequencies when m and n differ by one. Such unwanted signals will be on adjacent frequencies inside the RF filter bandwidth where they can cause interference.

For CW, FM and constant amplitude data systems a lack of linearity will not affect the reception of the signal. A non-linear class C amplifier can be used, resulting in greater efficiency but a harmonic filter is essential.

Output matching

Power amplifiers are designed to work into a specific load impedance. This should also be non-reactive. Amateur usage and most professional communications system use 50Ω. Failure to provide a 50Ω load risks current or voltage excursions outside the safe operating area of the active devices and consequent failure.

The actual load on the active device is probably not 50Ω. For a 12V PA producing 100W the current will be of the order of 16A. Even a crude calculation suggests the transistor is looking at something around 1Ω. That needs to be transformed up to 50Ω.

The output matching circuit does that and normally provides harmonic filtering as well. **Fig 4.15** shows an example. The circuit design is outside the scope of the syllabus. Typical circuits are π (pi) section filters that also provide impedance transformation and matching. The actual output impedance of a PA is not 50Ω, it is much less. Nonetheless, it does want to feed into a 50Ω resistive load.

Poor matching or unwanted feedback paths caused by stray coupling can result in unintended oscillation – parasitic oscillations. These could be at any frequency, causing considerable interference and may even damage the amplifier. Screens will minimise such coupling and series resistors in input circuits are often used to reduce the Q-factor of unintended resonances.

External amplifiers and ALC

External amplifiers introduce an addition risk of problems, apart that is from the sheer strength of the signal causing interference. The main risk is over-driving, feeding too much power into the amplifier, more than required for full output.

The non-linearities of a PA show up when driven hard. Ideally they should be run a bit below full power. The reduction will be quite unnoticeable at the receiver. The ALC on the

PA must be connected back to the driver rig or carefully monitored. It is the peaks on SSB that cause the problems. These include intermodulation products, resulting in splatter, and harmonics, potential interference to other bands and non-amateurs.

Receivers: receiver specifications

The RF quality of a receiver can be determined from a number of parameters that should be specified by the manufacturer.

Signal to noise ratio

The relative proportions of the wanted signal and unwanted noise. Two common measures, 10dB signal to noise and 12dB SINAD. SINAD is signal to noise and distortion. Any distortion products are regarded as additional noise. This level is useable but not particularly comfortable listening.

Minimum discernable signal

This is the weakest signal that will give a specified signal to noise ratio at the receiver output. It is a measure of how much noise is added by the receiver itself.

Dynamic Range

This is the range, usually specified in dB, between the minimum discernable signal and the largest signal that can be handled without overload. Overloading an amplifier results in non-linearity and spurious intermodulation products. These will limit the minimum discernable signal.

Bandwidth and selectivity

The bandwidth is the frequency range over which the signal is attenuated by less than 3dB. (Some specifications use 6dB). Selectivity refers to the rejection of unwanted signals and a rejection of 60dB is normally used. The 'shape factor' is the ratio of the 6dB to 60dB bandwidths and is an indication of the steepness of the sides of the filter response. That is how fast the receiver response drops once outside the wanted bandwidth. A good analogue filter can achieve a shape factor of 2, digital signal processing can do better and avoid some of the other artefacts of sharp filtering such as a tendency to ringing. That is the output from the filter continues after the input has ceased, rather like the sound from a bell some while after it has been struck.

Receiver architecture

The superhet remains the key block diagram and the only new concept is the double superhet. Remember the purpose of the superhet was to bring all the received signals down to a single frequency, the IF. As we shall see the choice of frequency can be a compromise and the double superhet avoids some of the issues. **Fig 4.16** shows the block diagram of a double superhet.

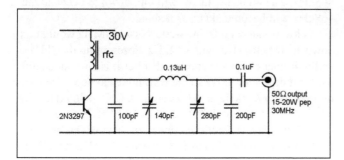

Fig 4.15. The output stage impedance matches the transistor collector load to 50Ω and low pass filters to suppress harmonics.

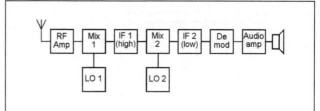

Fig 4.16. A double superhet receiver overcomes any compromises on choice of intermediate frequency.

RF Amplifier

The key issue at VHF and above is low noise. The amplifier's noise performance, coupled with filter bandwidths and the distribution of gain round the various stages in the receiver is critical to its performance. At HF the atmospheric noise is much higher so gain and noise performance is less of an issue. There are many high power broadcast stations and the dynamic range of the receiver is more critical. Switched filters in the front end may seek to limit the interference potential of the stronger stations and there is, now, a tendency, in the better receivers, to move away from general coverage reception, back to improved operation on the amateur bands.

Mixer

The mixer is a deliberately non-linear device and produces all the frequencies given by the formula quoted previously, $F = m \times f_1 + n \times f_2$. The wanted output will be $f_1 + f_2$ or $f_1 - f_2$. The other outputs are removed by filtering. Many general coverage HF receivers may use $f_1 + f_2$ to place the first IF above the tuning range, around 60 to 70MHz. The reason for that will soon become apparent.

If the wanted signal is at 7MHz and the LO is set to 6·5MHz, then the IF will be at 500kHz An RF signal at 6MHz will also produce a 500kHz IF. This is the 'Image Frequency' or 'Second Channel' and must be removed in the RF stage before the mixer. The separation between the wanted signal and the image is twice the IF. For easy RF filtering, this indicates a high IF.

A 2·8kHz wide SSB filter centred on 100kHz is much easier to implement than one centred on 1600kHz. For easy rejection of adjacent frequencies a low IF is desirable.

The double superhet has a high first IF to simplify image channel issues and a low second IF to simplify adjacent channel rejection. Some receivers employ as many as four IFs to achieve specific design goals. Each conversion stage brings its own problems and increases the risk of spurious signals in the receiver, seeming like a real RF signal but actually an internally generated false response.

Fig 4.17 shows a typical mixer circuit based on a dual-gate FET.

IF stages

The IF stage provides the bulk of the gain and the receiver selectivity. A typical circuit is shown in **Fig 4.18**. The IF trans-

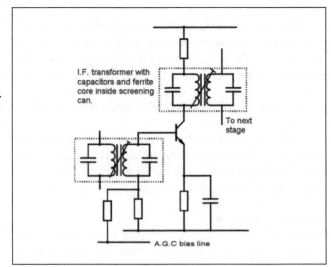

Fig 4.18. An IF amplifier circuit.

formers provide transformer coupling and selectivity. They are screened to minimise coupling to and from other stages.

The degree of coupling affects the frequency response. Loose coupling results in a shallow, low-Q response, progressing to a sharper response as the coupling increases. See **Fig 4.19**. Over-coupling results in a small dip in the middle of the responses curve. This may be a desirable feature to get a wider reasonably flat at top but with steep sides.

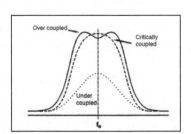

Fig 4.19. Frequency response of transformer coupled tuned circuits.

The AGC bias line reduces the base bias and limits the gain of the transistor. This causes distortion but the distortion products are mostly at harmonics of the IF and removed by the IF filters.

Demodulator

AM demodulation was covered at Intermediate level with Fig 4.10.

SSB demodulation requires a carrier insertion oscillator (CIO) and a product detector In fact this is simply a mixer being used as a demodulator. Consider an upper sideband audio signal occupying the frequency range 14·200 to 14·203MHz which has been mixed down to an IF of 465 to 468kHz. It is mixed down again in the product detector with the CIO set to 465kHz. The 465kHz 'audio' will mix down to 0Hz and the 468kHz will become 3kHz, as it should be.

A lower sideband from 14200 to 14·197MHz would mix down to 465-462kHz, with 462kHz representing the 3kHz audio. Rather than have another IF filter it is normal to shift the local oscillator 3kHz so the LSB mixes to 465 - 468, but remembering 465kHz is 0kHz audio. A CIO at 465kHz will result in the 3kHz 'audio' being produced at 0Hz and 0Hz 'audio' at 3kHz, ie frequency inverted. The CIO is reset to 468kHz to avoid this. In most receivers this is all accomplished inside the set based on the mode USB/LSB setting and the user is unaware of the finer details.

FM may be recovered using a ratio detector as shown in

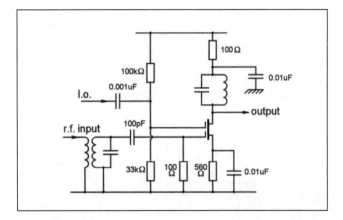

Fig 4.17. A mixer stage using a dual gate FET. The LO input is separate from the RF input to minimise the risk of the LO being radiated.

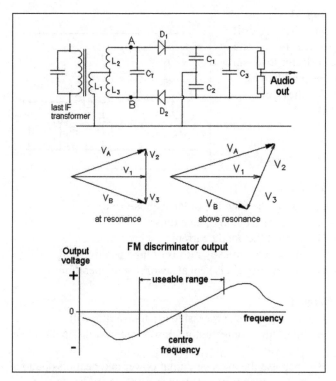

Fig 4.20. An FM discriminator; this circuit is a ratio detector.

Fig 4.20. The tuned circuit of L_2, L_3 and C_T is resonant at the centre frequency. The phase of the voltages across L_2 and L_3 are shifted by 90° with respect to L_1 by the resonant circuit. The voltage at point A is the vector sum of the voltages across L_1 and L_2, likewise B is the vector sum of voltages L_1 and L_3. At resonance they are of equal magnitude and are detected as equal but opposite voltages because D_1 and D_2 are reversed. Each side of resonance the magnitudes change little because the frequency range is narrow with respect to the bandwidth of the tuned circuit. The phases change more dramatically and give rise to a significant voltage change for relatively small frequency variations. The useable range is the linear portion of the response curve shown at the bottom of the figure.

Since data is often transmitted as some form of frequency shift, the above circuit may be used for data recovery, but there are other systems in use outside the scope of the syllabus.

Sample Questions

There are 13 questions on transmitters and receivers.

Question	Syllabus Item
23	4a.1, 4b.1, 4c.1
24	4d.1, 4e.1
25	4f.1, 4f.2, 4f.3
26	4g.1, 4g.2, 4g.3, 4g.4, 4g.5
27	4h.1, 4h.2
28	4h.3, 4h.4, 4h.5
29	4h.6, 4i.1
30	4j.1, 4j.2, 4j.3
31	4k.1
32	4l.1, 4n.2
33	4m.1, 4m.2, 4n.1
34	4o.1, 4p.1
35	4q.1, 4r.1

a4a1-1

The diagram shows an SSB transmitter. What is the function of the box marked '2'?

A Modulator.

B Mixer.

C Amplifier.

D Sideband filter.

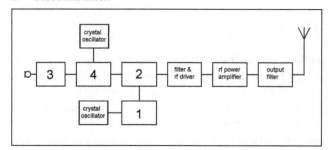

a4b1-1

The purpose of the transistor in a crystal oscillator is to

A offset the losses in the tuned circuit

B provide a low impedance output

C maintain the stability of the crystal

D stabilise the bias voltages on the crystal.

a4c1-1

The block diagram of a frequency synthesiser shows the division ratios and the crystal oscillator frequency. The output frequency is

A 100·4544MHz

B 432·0000MHz

C 436·0000MHz

D 2880·000MHz.

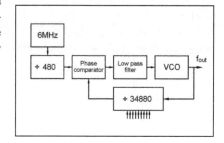

a4d1-1

A 9cm transmitter is used to produce an FM signal on 10·260GHz. The transmitter is likely to be set to a frequency of
A 3260MHz
B 3420MHz
C 3456MHz
D 3620MHz.

a4e1-1

The modulator of a multi-mode transceiver operates at 4·7MHz. To produce a signal at 14·1MHz band, the modulator output should be
A fed to a frequency tripler
B modulated onto the 14·1MHz carrier
C mixed with a clean signal on 9·4MHz
D filtered to remove the image on 11·7MHz.

a4f1-1

An FM transmission is regarded as 'narrow band' when
A only speech or audio signals below 3·5kHz are transmitted
B the deviation is less than 50% of the peak deviation for the system
C the modulation index is equal to or less than unity
D the deviation ratio does not exceed unity.

a4f2-1

What is the necessary bandwidth of an FM system with a peak deviation of 5kHz and a maximum audio frequency of 3·5kHz?
A 5kHz.
B 7kHz.
C 10kHz.
D 17kHz.

a4f3-1

A data transmitter feeds the binary data signal direct to the modulator of the transmitter, resulting in a 170Hz transmitted frequency shift between a data one and a data zero. The ITU designation for this type of modulation is F1B. Off-air this type of modulation is indistinguishable from a different type of data modulation; which one?
A Feeding the binary data to the microphone socket of an FM transmitter, F3B.
B Feeding the binary data to a modem producing two audio tones separated by 170Hz and feeding them to the microphone socket of an FM transmitter, F2B.
C Feeding the binary data to a modem producing two audio tones separated by 170Hz and feeding them to the microphone socket of an SSB transmitter, J2B.
D Feeding the binary data to the microphone socket of an SSB transmitter, J3B.

a4g1-1

Which type of modulation is NOT suitable for using a non-linear external RF power amplifier?
A Any type of modulation.
B CW modulation.
C SSB modulation.
D FM modulation.

a4g2-1

In the circuit diagram the collector load can be identified as
A the r.f.c.
B L1
C L1, C1-3 and the output
D the transistor.

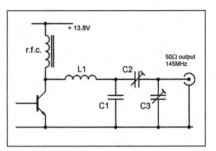

a4g3-1

In a valve, the function of the cathode is to
A produce a cloud of electrons
B control the anode current
C attract electrons by means of high positive voltage
D ensure the grid is kept at a working temperature.

a4g4-1

Employing speech processing in a transmitter will
A limit the average output power and heat dissipation to a safe value
B increase the average output power and heat dissipation
C reduce the average output power or heat dissipation
D not affect the average output power or heat dissipation.

a4g5-1

The ALC line between the transmitter and external power amplifier (PA)
A provides a signal from the transmitter to the PA to control the output power
B provides a signal from the PA to limit or reduce the transmitter output power
C allows the metering on the transmitter to show the relevant conditions in the PA
D prevent the PA from being over-modulated.

a4h1-1

The MOST significant effect of drift in a transmitter is that
A the distant receiver will have to retune periodically to maintain contact
B the received signal quality will be markedly impaired
C transmission may occur outside an amateur band
D interference may be caused to other amateurs.

a4h2-1

Fast edges on a Morse transmission will
A risk causing chirp on the transmission
B make the transmitted signal much wider than necessary
C simplify automatic reading of the signal at the receiver
D be uncomfortable to listen to at the receiving station.

a4h3-1

Using transformer coupling techniques between the various stages of a transmitter will help
A avoid earth loops in the transmitter and risk of instability
B achieve a good impedance match to the next stage
C reduce the chances of harmonic radiation
D avoid overdriving and non-linearity.

a4h4-1

The circuit diagram shows part of an amplifier for 144MHz. L2 and C2 resonate at 144MHz but there is an unwanted spurious signal caused by L1 and C1 resonating at 2MHz. This parasitic oscillation may be removed by

A   changing C1 from 100nF to 500nF

B   fitting another 100nF capacitor in parallel with L1

C   fitting a 10nF and 10Ω resistor in series from the bottom of L1 to the 0V line

D   fitting a 10nF and 10Ω resistor in series from the bottom of L2 to the 0V line.

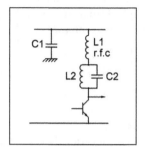

a4h5-1

Over-modulation is most likely to cause

A   unwanted radiation on harmonics of the RF transmitted signal

B   interference caused by harmonics of the audio signal

C   inadequate suppression of the unwanted sideband

D   frequency instability in the transmitted signal.

a4h6-1

A frequency synthesiser may produce the wrong output if

A   the 'out of lock' signal loses control of the VCO in the synthesiser

B   the signals into the phase comparator are on different frequencies

C   division ratios of the programmable divider and crystal divider are different

D   temperature stability of the VCO is not maintained.

a4i1-1

Overdriving an external power amplifier (PA) may cause intermodulation products because

A   the PA will be operated outside its linear range

B   the ALC action will try to shut down the PA

C   the ALC is too slow to respond to the modulation envelope

D   excessive current will flow in the PA output transistors.

a4j1-1

The graph shows the frequency response of a radio receiver. The offset at the accepted level to quote selectivity is approximately

A   3kHz

B   6kHz

C   8kHz

D   20kHz.

a4j2-1

A radio receiver can just resolve a signal at a level of 0·16µV (-123dBm) and the maximum signal before overloading is 10mV (-27dBm). What is its dynamic range?

A   27dB.

B   96dB.

C   123dB.

D   150dB.

a4j3-1

A radio receiver is being checked and a 0·2µV SSB signal at the RF input produces a 1V tone at the audio output together with noise averaging 100mV. The signal to noise ratio is

A   10dB

B   20dB

C   0dBV

D   -121dBm.

a4k1-1

The diagram shows a double superhet for HF that mixes all incoming signals to a first IF above the HF band. To what frequency should LO2 be set?

A   12·650MHz

B   38·900MHz

C   66·400MHz

D   69·700MHz.

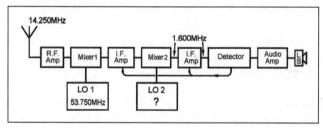

a4l1-1

A radio receiver is specified as having a lowest resolvable signal of 5µV (-123dBW) and a maximum signal without overload of 158mV (-33dBW). Fitting a preamp of 10dB gain results in the lowest resolvable signal of 3µV (-127dBW). What change is there in the dynamic range of the new system?

A   Increased by 4dB.

B   No change.

C   Reduced by 4dB.

D   Reduced by 6dB.

a4m1-1

A general coverage receiver is required to tune over the range 600kHz to 1600kHz and uses readily available IF components at 465kHz. The best choice for the local oscillator tuning range is

A   135kHz - 1350kHz

B   465kHz - 1465kHz

C   600kHz - 1600kHz

D   1065kHz - 2065kHz.

a4m2-1

A wideband scanner picks up a good CW signal when tuned to 3·61MHz but picks up the same signal when tuned to 7·51MHz. A reason for this might be that the

A   transmitter has a strong second harmonic

B   receiver intermediate frequency is 1·95MHz

C   signal on 3·61MHz is overloading the receiver

D   transmitter key click filter is faulty.

a4n1-1

The factor suggesting a low intermediate frequency should be used in a receiver design is that

A   image frequency rejection is simplified

B   the tuning range of the local oscillator is reduced

C   oscillation due to stray capacitances is less likely to occur

D   the rejection of adjacent channel interference is easier to accomplish.

a4n2-1

A feature of an over-coupled response in an IF transformer is that

A   the bandwidth is markedly reduced making the configuration ideal for CW reception

B   the -3dB bandwidth is wider than other coupling methods with minimal effect on the response at -30 or -60 dB

C   the increased coupling allows lower gain in the IF transistors with consequent reduction in likelihood of oscillations.

D   the distortions caused by reduced AGC bias are significantly reduced.

a4o1-1

Demodulation of an FM signal is normally achieved by a circuit which

A   relies on the slope of a tuned circuit producing amplitude changes in response to the frequency changes of the signal

B   times the period between successive cycles to determine the exact frequency of the signal

C   mixes the signal with a known reference frequency to determine the instantaneous frequency offset

D   uses changes in phase angle in a tuned circuit to give different voltages, which may then be rectified.

a4p1-1

The signal which forms the AGC control voltage is derived from the

A   average signal level seen in the demodulator stage

B   input to the IF stages and used to control the IF gain

C   output of the first mixer, before the gain is high enough to risk overloading

D   biasing of the transistors in the IF amplifier stages of the receiver.

a4q1-1

The homemade converter shown in the drawing is intended to be connected to an HF receiver operating in the 28 - 30MHz band. Which amateur band is it intended for?

A   2m.

B   4m.

C   6m.

D   10m.

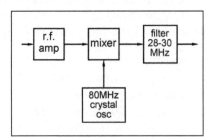

a4q1-2

The converter shown in the drawing for question a4q1-1 has an unfortunate design problem. What is it?

A   The oscillators in the transverter and receiver are in different enclosures so may suffer different temperature related drifts.

B   The received frequency will decrease as the frequency on the HF receiver is increased, because the transverter oscillator is above the received frequency.

C   It will be necessary to add 28MHz to all the frequencies displayed on the HF receiver.

D   The system will be unsuitable for receiving SSB signals because the sidebands are reversed in the mixing process.

5. Feeders and Antennas

FOUNDATION

Coaxial cable is most commonly used for radio frequencies and is shown in **Fig 5.1**. The field is contained within the cable by the outer braided screen. The braid must make continuous contact with the metal body of the plugs and sockets to maintain the shielding.

Correct RF plugs and sockets must be used. Common types are the PL259 and BNC. N-type may also be seen at higher frequencies or with larger diameter cables.

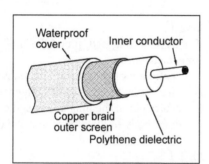

Fig 5.1. Coaxial cable is most commonly used for RF feeders.

The dipole

The basic antenna is the dipole. It is half a wavelength ($\lambda/2$) long, which means it is designed for a particular frequency. The dipole radiates best from the side. Held vertically it will radiate equally to all points on the horizon but not straight up or straight down. If fixed horizontally in a North-South direction, the maximum radiation will be to the East and West. The antenna converts the RF currents in the feeder to an electromagnetic wave, a radio wave. It works equally well receiving as transmitting and has the same directional properties.

The quarter wave ground-plane is a development of the dipole; it is a vertical dipole but with the bottom half removed leaving just the top half, which is a quarter wavelength ($\lambda/4$) long. To work properly it requires either a metal ground plane, such as a car roof if mounted in the centre, or radials, that is horizontal 'spokes', also $\lambda/4$ long. Normally three or four are used. **Fig 5.2** shows the dipole and the $\lambda/4$ ground-plane.

The 5/8 λ ground plane has a matching coil at the base and has 'gain'. This is achieved by focussing more of the radiation in the wanted direction; in this case horizontally rather than upwards. The gain is defined as the signal from the subject antenna compared to a reference one, usually a dipole. It should be noted that gain is always achieved by focussing. The total radiated power over all directions is unchanged. This gain also applies on receive.

The Yagi

Further gain is offered by the Yagi. The 5/8 λ compresses the vertical radiation so it was mostly horizontal, the Yagi compresses in both dimensions forming a beam, rather like that from a torch. The Yagi must be pointed towards the distant station. The Yagi and 5/8 λ are shown in **Fig 5.3**.

Since the signal in the wanted direction is now stronger, the ERP, effective radiated power, gives an indication of how much power would be needed to a dipole to produce the same strength signal as our antenna does.

$$\text{ERP} = \text{power to antenna} \times \text{antenna gain}$$

Note: Often the gain of an antenna is quoted in a scientific unit, the dB, decibel. This formula does not use the dB, the gain must be expressed in normal numbers, a gain of three, for example, means the signal is three times as strong. The dB is explained in the Advanced part of Section 3.

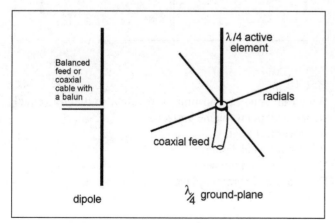

Fig 5.2. Dipole and ground plane antennas.

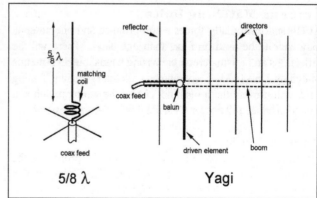

Fig 5.3. The 5/8 λ and the Yagi antennas. Both these antennas exhibit gain.

Balance and Polarisation

The dipole is a balanced antenna, that is it is symmetrical, both to look at and electrically. Each half of the dipole requires an equal but opposite signal. Conversely, the ground-plane antenna has only one radiating element and the radials are earthed. That is an unbalanced antenna. The driven element in a Yagi is a dipole so it is balanced.

Coaxial cable has one live centre conductor and an earthed outer. It is unbalanced. It is ideal for feeding a ground plane or end-fed long wire but not a dipole or Yagi. A 'balun' is used to convert the unbalanced signal from the coaxial cable to the balanced feed for those antennas.

The dipole and Yagi can be mounted with the elements vertical or horizontal. That will determine the polarisation of the radio wave. At HF that is not too critical, but at VHF and UHF it is important that the antennas at each end of the 'contact' have the same polarisation.

Matching

Antennas have a 'feed resistance', that is they appear to absorb power as if they were replaced by a resistor. Of course they actually radiate that power, but the transmitter will not know the difference. They also must be the correct size for the intended frequency, a dipole is $\lambda/2$ long. At other frequencies the 'feed resistance' will be wrong and some of the power up the feeder from the transmitter will be reflected at the antenna input. It is not radiated but reflected back down the feeder to the transmitter. The antenna is not now 'matched' to the feeder. The reflected power will also result in the wrong match at the transmitter. In severe cases this could result in damage to the transmitter and the transmitter protection circuits may cut the output power to reduce the risk. Nonetheless transmitting into a non-matched feeder should be avoided.

Standing waves

The reflected signal will combine with the forward signal (from the transmitter) to form standing waves in the feeder. These cannot be seen but a standing wave ratio (SWR) meter can measure them. There are two types. One shows the forward and reverse signal on two meters, the other simply shows the standing wave ratio. When correctly matched, there is no reverse signal, ie no reflected power and the SWR meter will read unity. Ideally the lowest SWR should be sought, preferably below 1·5 and certainly below 2. At VHF and UHF values below 1·3 should be achieved without too much difficulty.

The full meaning of SWR is left to a later course.

Antenna Matching Units

At HF space normally forces a compromise and one antenna may have to be used on more than one band. There will be reflections and mismatch on the wrong bands, but an Antenna Matching Unit (AMU), sometimes called an Antenna Tuning Unit, will prevent the transmitter seeing the wrong match and able to produce full power. Not ideal but often neccessary.

Dummy loads

For testing a transmitter or investigating EMC problems, the transmitter is connected to a dummy load. This is a high power screened resistor of 50Ω; the standard antenna feed resistance. The transmitter will work normally but very little radiation will occur. An SWR meter will show a value of one, or no reflected power.

Sample Questions

Three questions are asked in this area.

Question	Syllabus Item
14	5a.1, 5a.2
15	5b.1, 5b.2, 5c.1, 5c.2, 5c.3
16	5c.4, 5c.5, 5d.1, 5e.1, 5e.2, 5f.1

f5a1-1
The diagram shows different types of cable, which one is suitable for radio frequencies?
A   Cable A.
B   Cable B.
C   Cable C.
D   Cable D.

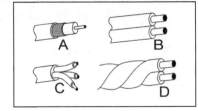

f5a2-1
When connecting BNC plugs, the braid of the cable should be connected to the
A   centre pin of the plug at both ends of the cable
B   outer body of the plug at both ends of the cable
C   centre pin of the plug at one end of the cable
D   outer body of the plug at one end of the cable.

f5b1-1
The antenna
A   will only pick up the wanted signal
B   converts electrical signals into radio waves
C   can be tuned to pick up FM or SSB signals
D   always radiates equally in all directions.

f5b2-1
The antenna shown in the diagram is a
A   dipole for the 10m band
B   Yagi for the 10m band
C   dipole for the 20m band
D   quarter wave for the 20m band.

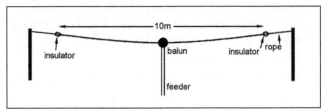

f5c1-1
Which antenna has an omni-directional radiation (equal signal to all points on the horizon)?
A   A vertical Yagi.
B   A horizontal dipole.
C   An end-fed long wire.
D   A 5/8 wave ground-plane.

f5c2-1

The gain shown by a Yagi antenna is due to its
A correct matching to the feeder
B ability to focus signals in one direction
C omni-directional coverage
D ability to be horizontal or vertical.

f5c3-1

If 10W is fed to a Yagi which has a gain of 5 times, the effective radiated power (ERP) in the best direction is
A 2W
B 5W
C 10W
D 50W.

f5c4-1

A dipole antenna is intended to work on the 20m band but is used on the 24m band. One effect of doing this is that
A the wavelength of the transmitted signal will be too long
B antenna could be damaged during long transmissions
C some power from the transmitter will be reflected back down the feeder
D the feeder will also have to be lengthened in order to match the antenna.

f5c5-1

Due to restricted space in the garden, the only HF dipole antenna is a half wave long on 14MHz. When used on other frequencies a device is fitted between the transmitter and feeder, that device is
A an SWR meter
B an AMU
C a low pass filter
D a frequency meter.

f5d1-1

The purpose of a Balun is to
A reduce the SWR on the feeder if the antenna is used on the wrong frequency
B allow a balanced antenna to be connected to unbalanced coaxial feeder.
C allow a balanced antenna to be connected to balanced feeder
D avoid a mis-match between the feeder and the transmitter output.

f5e1-1

A correct match to the antenna is indicated by
A an SWR meter showing minimum reflected power
B an SWR meter showing maximum reflected power
C a power meter showing minimum forward (transmitted) power
D a power meter showing maximum forward (transmitted) power.

f5e2-1

When starting a regular contact on 2m, it is noticed that the SWR meter is reading rather higher than usual. You should suspect that
A there is a fault in the transmitter
B the fault must be in the feeder
C the fault must be in the antenna
D the fault is in the feeder or antenna.

f5f1-1

The purpose of the dummy load is to
A provide the correct tension on long wire antennas
B absorb the unwanted power reflected from the antenna
C use in place of an antenna when checking the transmitter
D prevent unwanted radiation escaping back down the power leads.

INTERMEDIATE

Coaxial and twin feeders

At Intermediate level we look at another type of feeder, balanced twin. It is simply two wires side by side. Ribbon feeder has a polythene spacer as shown in **Fig 5.4** and open wire twin is made from two separate wires with spacers, rather like a ladder.

Radiation is avoided since the equal and opposite currents cause equal and opposite fields that cancel out. Objects close to such feeder may imbalance the field and cause some radiation. It is rather harder to install. This difficulty does not arise with coaxial cable since the field is contained within the cable.

Balanced feeder typically has a lower loss than coaxial cable but in both cases the losses increase with length and affect transmit and receive equally.

Coax is 'unbalanced'; it has a live conductor and an earthed outer screen. Without the screen the inner conductor would radiate. Antennas may be balanced, eg the dipole, or unbalanced, eg a vertical of some kind.

Connecting balanced and unbalanced items together will result in currents flowing down the outside of the coaxial cable and unbalancing the currents in the balanced feeder. This will result in feeder radiation, risking interference and will distort the radiation pattern of the antenna.

The balun is a device permitting balanced and unbalanced devices to be safely connected. It may or may not alter the feed impedance seen by the feeder, depending on construction. Impedance matching and balancing are two separate issues and each may require separate attention.

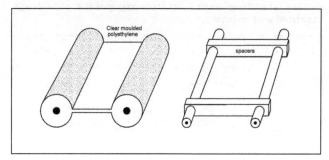

Fig 5.4. Twin feeders. Ribbon and open-wire 'ladder' feeder.

Characteristic Impedance

Feeder has a characteristic impedance related to the capacitance between the conductors and their inductance. This, in turn, depends on the diameter and spacing of twin feeder or the two diameters of coaxial cable. Impedance is not relevant to DC but does affect RF behaviour and the matching of feeder to the transmitter and antenna. All three should be designed to have the same value, which is 50Ω in amateur practice. When correctly terminated, the ratio of the RF potential difference to the RF current in a feeder will be equal to the characteristic impedance. This will not be the case for a feeder terminated in some other value.

Open wire feeder typically has a higher impedance, 75Ω to 600Ω being the most common.

Antenna feeds

Antennas have a feed point impedance that is the ratio of RF PD to current at their input. It is determined by the antenna dimensions and the frequency. The correct impedance will only occur at the designed frequency. For the dipole, this is approximately 50Ω.

If the antenna feed point impedance is not the same as the characteristic impedance of the feeder, some of the incident energy will be reflected back towards the transmitter. There is now an RF signal flowing in both directions in the feeder. At points along the feeder, these two signals will combine to produce high voltages with voltage minima midway between them. This is shown in **Fig 5.5**. The same applies to the RF currents, with current maxima at the voltage minima. These are 'standing waves'.

The reflected signal will alter the PD and current all along the feeder and will affect the impedance seen by the transmitter. A device known as an antenna matching unit (AMU) or antenna tuning unit (ATU) can change the impedance presented to the transmitter. It does not actually tune the antenna; that is done by cutting it to the correct length. It does, however, bring the antenna / feeder / AMU system to 50Ω resistive, allowing the transmitter to produce full power without the risk of damage.

An AMU does not affect the SWR on the antenna side or improve what might be a poor radiation pattern due to operating at the wrong frequency. **Fig 5.6** shows the connection of a transmitter, SWR meter, AMU, feeder and antenna. The AMU is adjusted so the meter indicates forward power but minimum reverse power. The power reflected *from* the antenna will not see the AMU as 50Ω and will be reflected back towards the antenna. Mostly the power is radiated but the feeder losses do increase.

If the SWR changes unexpectedly, something has happened to the antenna or feeder, not the transmitter. An increased SWR suggests an antenna fault or broken connection. A low SWR (that is, lower than previously achieved) is not an improvement and is probably an indication of water in the feeder or other reason for increased feeder losses. Remember, the SWR shows the reflected power. If the feeder losses double for some reason, the power reaching the antenna will halve and the amount reflected, even from a good antenna, will halve too. That reflected signal will be halved again by the time it gets back to the SWR meter and transmitter, but the SWR indication will have apparently "improved" considerably. Check it out!

Antenna Polar diagrams

Fig 5.7 shows the polar diagram or radiation pattern of a dipole. The polar diagram indicates the direction of maximum radiation. To interpret the diagram, consider a line from the centre of the dipole to cut the polar diagram. The length of that line gives the strength of the radiation in that direction. Maximum radiation is at right-angles to the dipole, ie broadside, and minimum off the ends.

In the Yagi, a reflector and two directors have been added to the dipole. Now the maximum radiation is in one direction and the signal in that direction will be much stronger. It will also receive better from that direction.

Fig 5.8 shows the polar diagrams of the λ/4 ground-plane and the 5/8 λ antennas. They are mounted vertically so the

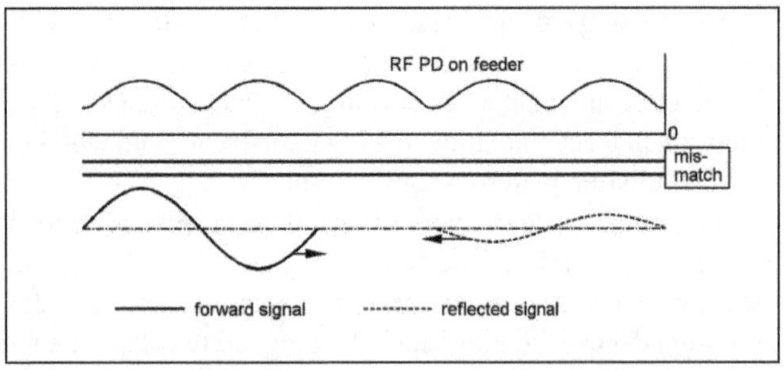

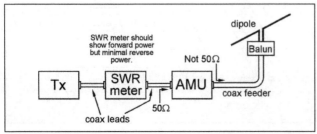

Fig 5.5. A mismatched load reflects some energy and causes standing waves. Stationary points of voltage maxima and minima.

Fig 5.6. Connecting a transmitter, SWR meter, AMU, feeder and antenna.

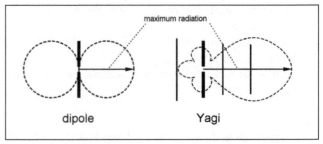

Fig 5.7. The polar diagram of a dipole and Yagi antennas.

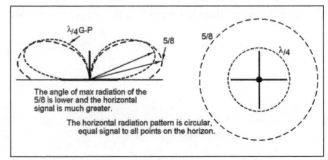

Fig 5.8. The vertical and horizontal polar diagrams of the λ/4 and 5/8 λ ground-plane antennas.

polar diagram is a vertical section. Also shown is the horizontal diagram, which is a bird's-eye view from overhead.

Sample Questions

The Intermediate examination paper will have three questions.

Question	Syllabus Item
25	5a.1 5a.2 5a.3 5a.4 5a.5 5b.1
26	5c.1 5d.1 5e.1
27	5f.1 5f.2 5f.3 5f.4 5f.5 5g.1

i5a1-1
The feeder suitable for direct connection to the centre of a dipole antenna is
A   coaxial cable
B   twin feeder
C   unbalanced feeder
D   of 300Ω impedance.

i5a2-1
The reason twin feeder does not radiate is that the
A   fields round each conductor are equal and in phase
B   fields round each conductor are equal and opposite
C   two conductors both have earthed screens
D   two conductors have a common earthed screen.

i5a3-1
In a correctly terminated coaxial cable the RF field
A   exists only within the cable and external objects have no effect
B   exists only within the cable but external objects can have an effect
C   is cancelled out by equal and opposite currents, so external objects have no effect
D   is concentrated by the outer screen resulting in external object having some effect.

i5a4-1
Which one of the feeders below will have the greatest loss?
A   10m of twin feeder.
B   20m of twin feeder.
C   10m of coaxial feeder.
D   20m of coaxial feeder.

i5a5-1
A transmitter produces 60W of RF to the feeder, which has a loss of 6dB. The power at the antenna connection will be
A   10W
B   15W
C   30W
D   54W.

i5b1-1
If the feeder is correctly terminated, the ratio of the RF potential difference to the RF current is determined by the
A   length of the feeder
B   output of the transmitter
C   relative dimensions of the conductors
D   wavelength of the transmitted signal.

i5c1-1
The feed point impedance of an antenna is dependant on the
A   gain and directivity of the antenna
B   proportion of power reflected back down the feeder
C   degree to which the antenna is a good match for the feeder
D   dimensions of the antenna in relation to the wavelength of the signal.

i5d1-1
Standing waves on a feeder are an indication that
A   the antenna feed point impedance is the same as that of the feeder
B   the signal from the transmitter is being radiated by the antenna
C   the transmitter will see a different impedance to that of the feeder
D   power is being reflected at the transmitter.

i5e1-1
The purpose of an Antenna Tuning Unit is to
A   adjust the antenna to the correct length for the transmitted signal
B   match the wavelength of the signal to that of the antenna
C   change the impedance the feeder presents to the transmitter
D   resonate the antenna at the transmitted frequency.

i5f1-1
Which drawing shows the polar diagram of a dipole antenna?
A   Polar plot A.
B   Polar plot B.
C   Polar plot C.
D   Polar plot D.

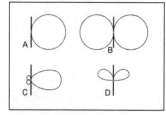

i5f2-1
An antenna for the 70cm band has a gain of 13dB and is fed with an RF power of 30W. What is the ERP?
A   30W.
B   43W.
C   340W.
D   600W.

i5f3-1
Which is the shortest RF element on a Yagi
A   director
B   reflector
C   boom
D   driven element.

i5f4-1
In a radio wave the electric field and the magnetic field are
A   parallel and define the plane of polarisation
B   at right angles and the electric field defines the plane of polarisation
C   at right angles and the magnetic field defines the plane of polarisation
D   at right angles and the electric field defines the direction of propagation.

i5f5-1

It is less important to use the same antenna polarisation for the sending and receiving stations on HF than VHF because

A at HF there is usually insufficient room to erect antennas with both polarisations

B the antennas are a fraction of a wavelength from the ground and have no polarisation

C either the electric or magnetic field will be horizontal and both are suitable for HF reception

D the polarisation after ionospheric reflection is can be quite different from that transmitted.

i5g1-1

The drawing shows 4 possible constructions of a dummy load. Without considering their power handling, which construction would be most suitable?

A Dummy load A.

B Dummy load B.

C Dummy load C.

D Dummy load D.

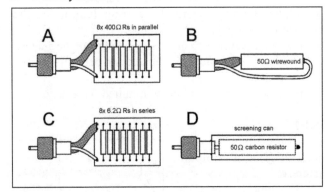

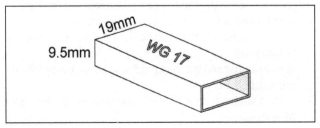

ADVANCED

Losses and Velocity factor of a feeder

The speed of propagation in a feeder is always less than that in free space. For open wire line it is about 0·95, around 0·9 for air-spaced coaxial feeder and 0·67 (or 2/3) for solid dielectric polythene feeder. The length of solid feeder for a quarter-wave line will be 2/3 of its free-space length.

Losses increase with frequency and become significant at VHF and UHF. The 6mm diameter coax used for interconnections is far too lossy at UHF. 10mm diameter cable, such as UR67 / RG217 is a minimum requirement and better cables are readily available. In the microwave region waveguides become the preferred choice. These are usually rectangular section 'tubes' of precise construction joined by flanges with the size determined by frequency. **Fig 5.9** shows a section of waveguide. The larger dimension is between a half and a full wavelength at the intended frequency. The size shown is suit-

Fig 5.9. A section of waveguide.

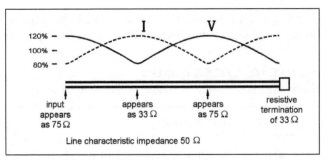

Fig 5.10. Standing waves on a mis-matched feeder. The impedance varies at half-wave intervals along the line.

able for 10GHz.

Fig 5.10 shows standing waves on a feeder. The voltage minima coincide with current maxima. At that point the impedance, looking towards the load, will be at a minimum. A quarter wave in either direction will see a voltage maxima and current minima. The impedance will be a maximum. This situation allows us to deliberately use a $\lambda/4$ line to change the impedance.

Consider stacking two 50Ω Yagis for extra gain. Paralleling them would result in a 25Ω input. We need to transform each Yagi to 100Ω so they parallel to 50Ω.

The formula is:

$$Z_0 = \sqrt{Z_{in} \times Z_{out}}$$

where Z_0 is the characteristic impedance required of the line, Z_{in} is the desired input impedance (100Ω) and Z_{out} is the actual load on the far end of the line (50Ω).

The line impedance required is 70·7Ω. 70Ω and 75Ω feeders are available, 75Ω particularly so since it is used for TV down-lead.

So using two tails each $\lambda/4$ long and paralleling them to a 50Ω feeder will do the job. The hardest bit is probably waterproofing the join.

SWR

The SWR is defined as:

$$SWR = \frac{V_{max}}{V_{min}} = \frac{V_f + V_r}{V_f - V_r}$$

where V_f is the voltage of the forward wave and V_r the voltage of the reverse wave.

Return loss

Return loss is defined as the ratio of the reflected signal to the forward signal, in dB.

$$Return\ loss = 10\ Log\ \frac{reflected\ power}{forward\ power}\ dB$$

Although the formula will give a negative sign, it is omitted in practice since the word 'loss' appears in the title. The title is a bit of a misnomer since there is no loss as such; the power not reflected is radiated, as it should be.

If 20% of the voltage is reflected at the antenna, then that represents 4% of the power. The return loss would be 14dB and the SWR 1+0·2/(1-0·2) which is 1·5:1. If 50% of the voltage is reflected the return loss would be ¼ or 6dB and the SWR 1·5/0·5 which is 3:1. All of the power reflected gives a zero return loss and an infinite SWR. Conversely, a perfect match is an infinite return loss and 1:1 SWR.

For 100% reflection and a line with 3dB loss (half power),

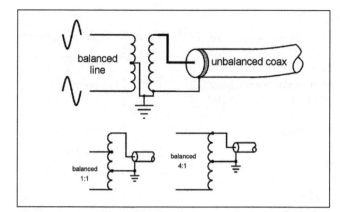

Fig 5.11. A transformer balun. The impedance ratio can be set by varying the number of turns on the two windings.

the return loss will be 6dB since only a quarter of the power will be returned to the source. The return loss at the source will always be equal to the return loss at the antenna plus twice the line loss.

Baluns

There are three types we need to consider. The transformer balun is shown in **Fig 5.11**. The two windings can be kept separate or used as an auto-transformer to provide 1:1 and 4:1 impedance ratios. Remember the impedance ratio is the square of the turns ratio.

A choke balun is simply a number of ferrite rings or large beads, possibly up to 30, over the feeder, preventing any current flowing in the outer surface of the braid. At VHF and UHF coiling the feeder, say 10 turns, or a few turns on a ferrite ring may suffice.

The sleeve balun is shown in **Fig 5.12**. It can only be used on a single band, but is easy to construct.

Antennas

The dipole is λ/2 long and, in practice, would be cut to that length and trimmed for the lowest SWR either in the centre of the band or where the user intends to operate. A correction factor for 'end effects' of 5% is typical; the antenna will probably end up at about 95% of the free-space length. Nonetheless, it is preferable to cut long and trim carefully.

Proximity to the ground will have an effect. Proximity is measured in wavelength so at VHF and UHF the antenna may be reasonably clear of the ground and other objects. At HF

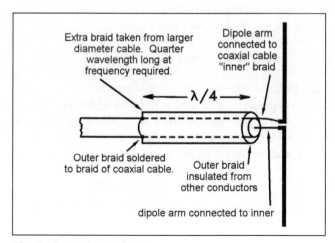

Fig 5.12. A sleeve balun.

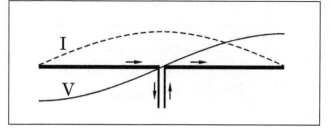

Fig 5.13. Current and voltage distribution on a dipole.

ground proximity causes the maximum radiation to be pushed upwards rather than horizontal. The angle at which the maximum occurs is known as the *Angle of Radiation*. For long distance communication a low angle is desirable and might be better achieved with a vertical antenna, although a large number of radials are usually required.

Feed impedance

Fig 5.13 shows the current and voltage distribution on a resonant dipole. The solid line shows the magnitude of the voltage and the dotted line, the current. The arrows show the direction of current flow at one instant. Half a cycle later they will all be reversed. The λ/4 ground plane is a simple development of the dipole. One half of the dipole is stood vertically on an 'RF mirror', the ground plane. The lower half of the dipole appears as a reflection in the mirror. The current at the base is a maximum and the voltage at the tip is a maximum.

For a thin wire dipole the feed impedance at the centre is 73Ω resistive. Off resonance the resistive portion changes slowly but a reactive component is introduced. A fat dipole using tubing at VHF/UHF or a small nest of parallel wires at HF has a slightly lower feed impedance and a wider bandwidth. The λ/4 ground plane has a 36Ω feed, ie half the dipole. Drooping the radials increases the feed impedance slightly but adds a reactive component.

The 5/8 λ antenna has a loading coil at the base which adds an extra λ/8 bringing the total to ¾λ. That is also a resistive feed and is a good match to 50Ω. The quad loop antenna with a reflector exhibits a 75Ω feed and, like the dipole, is balanced. A balun will be needed. The actual feed impedance depends on the exact circumference and spacing. On its own a quad loop exhibits over 100Ω.

The proximity of the ground or nearby conductors affects the feed impedance. The signal is reflected back and induces currents in the antenna. The actual impedance depends on the size of the reflection and the phase difference but within λ/4 the impedance is reduced. This is most noticeable in the Yagi where the feed impedance can be significantly reduced. To combat this a folded dipole is used, shown in **Fig 5.14**. If the current in the two sections are equal then the feed current is halved for the same total power. Consequently the input impedance increases by a factor of four. Doubly folded (three conductors) has nine times the feed impedance.

The size of HF antennas forces a compromise and a parallel tuned circuit can act as a trap or insulator at a spe-

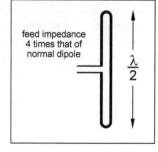

feed impedance 4 times that of normal dipole

Fig 5.14. A folded dipole.

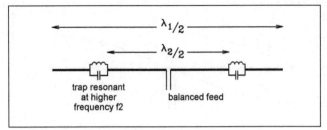

Fig 5.15. A trap dipole can resonate on more than one frequency band.

cific frequency. **Fig 5.15** shows a trap dipole. The trap is resonant on the higher frequency and isolates the outer portion of the antenna. Two traps will allow a dipole resonant on three bands. Below resonance the trap appears inductive and act as a small loading coil. That shortens the overall length of the dipole. The technique can be extended to Yagis. A three element tri-band Yagi, for example, will have 12 traps in total.

Antenna Matching Units

Typical AMU (ATU) circuits are shown in **Fig 5.16**. Fig 5.16A is a general purpose design capable of a wide range of matching but with the possibility of high circulating currents and voltages. Fig 5.16B shows a π (pi) match, also fairly wide ranging and Fig 5.16C the T-match, less common but used where impedances are higher. Omitting one section to form an L match can be done where the reactive component of the antenna is known.

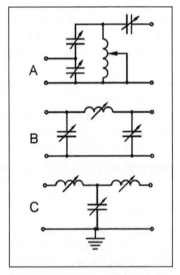

Fig 5.16. Types of antenna matching units. In practice all three will be earthed.

The AMU performs two functions. It provides an opposite reactance to that of the antenna or antenna / feeder and also can transform the resistive component to 50Ω, resulting in a purely resistive input required by the transmitter. The SWR on the antenna side is unaffected and the feeder length, on the antenna side, is part of the system and may also act as an impedance transformer.

Sample Questions

There are five questions to be answered in the Advanced paper, distributed as shown.

Question	Syllabus Item
36	5a.1, 5a.2, 5a.3, 5b.1
37	5c.1, 5c.2, 5c.3
38	5c.4, 5c.5
39	5d.1, 5d.2, 5d.3
40	5e.1

a5a1-1

The drawing shows two 70MHz Yagis stacked together with λ/4 tails of solid poly-thene coax to the splitter for impedance matching. What length are the tails?

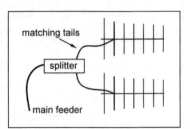

A 71cm.
B 107cm.
C 143cm.
D 214cm.

a5a2-1

The antennas in the drawing for a5a1-1 each have a feed impedance of 50Ω, but this needs to be transformed to 100Ω so the two antennas can be fed in parallel. What should the characteristic impedance of the feeder be to achieve this?

A 50Ω.
B 70Ω.
C 75Ω.
D 100Ω.

a5a3-1

Waveguide would be appropriate to use at a frequency of

A 435MHz
B 1296MHz
C 3420MHz
D 10460MHz.

a5b1-1

The drawing shows a

A sleeve balun
B choke balun
C 1:1 balun
D 4:1 balun.

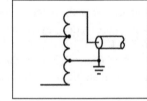

a5c1-1

The length of an HF dipole for 14MHz should be

A 7·1m
B 10·2m
C 10·7m
D 21·4m.

a5c2-1

To achieve longer distances using HF the radiated signal should

A have a high angle of radiation
B have a low angle of radiation
C be directed towards a great circle
D be directed away from a great circle.

a5c3-1

A 70m dipole is fitted with a reflector and a number of directors to achieve greater gain but it is found the SWR has risen markedly. A possible solution is to

A shorten the length of the dipole elements
B lengthen the feeder by λ/4
C add a conductor to create a folded dipole
D swap the positions of the director and reflectors.

a5c4-1

The antenna shown in the drawing is a

A λ/4 ground plane
B 5/8 λ antenna
C quad antenna
D trapped antenna.

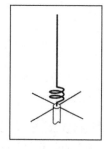

a5c5-1

A wire dipole antenna is fitted with two parallel tuned circuits in each half of the dipole. The purpose of this is to

A reduce the overall length of the dipole
B allow the dipole to resonate on two bands
C allow the dipole to resonate on three bands
D increase the impedance to match open wire feeder.

a5d1-1

A poorly matched antenna results in half the incident power being reflected. Neglecting feeder losses the SWR will be about

A 1·5:1
B 2:1
C 3:1
D 6:1.

a5d2-1

A well matched antenna will exhibit a

A high return loss and low SWR
B high return loss and high SWR
C low return loss and low SWR
D low return loss and high SWR.

a5d3-1

A new antenna shows a return loss of 23dB when measured in the shack. If the feeder loss is 2dB, the return loss at the antenna connection will be

A 19dB
B 21dB
C 25dB
D 27dB.

a5e1-1

The impedance seen looking into the feeder termination in the shack is seen to be 200Ω resistive and a capacitive reactance of 30Ω. To bring this to 50Ω resistive for the transmitter it will be necessary to use an

A ATU
B ATU and a 4:1 transformer
C ATU and a 1:1 balun
D ATU and a 4:1 balun.

6. Propagation

From a distance the antenna looks like a point source and the radio waves spread out, travelling in straight lines. This can be viewed as a torch beam or a paint sprayer, the beam or the spray gets weaker as the distance is increased because it is trying to cover a greater area.

There are three ways a radio wave can change direction. They can bounce off a reflecting object, usually something conductive, a large metal hanger or the side of a large glass building, where the 'sun-dim' coating is often partially conductive. They can be bent or 'refracted' in the ionosphere and they can diffract round large solid objects.

At HF a building is small compared to a wavelength so shadowing is minimal, but at VHF and UHF shadows behind large buildings and behind hills can be very noticeable and close behind a hill may have no useable signal. Further away, the diffraction over the top will fill in the shadow and the signal may be useable again until it fades out due to distance.

The ionosphere and HF

The ionosphere, conductive gases at heights from 70 to 400km, can bend HF signals back towards the earth. The bending ability depends on the level of ionisation caused by the ultraviolet light from the sun. This varies over the 24-hour cycle, from summer to winter, and also due to changes in sunspots, effects on the surface of the sun, which varies over an 11-year cycle (although you don't need to remember the last point until the Intermediate exam). The bending is also dependent on the frequency; higher frequencies are bent less and may not get bent back to the earth's surface at all. Note that the HF signal is correctly described as being *refracted* back. It is continuously curved back, not bounced or reflected.

World-wide coverage is possible at HF. Each 'hop' can be up to 4000km but the wave can bounce off the earth's surface and be refracted in the ionosphere again. Part of the skill and fun of amateur radio is finding out which bands are open to which areas of the word at which times of day.

VHF and UHF

VHF and UHF propagation is mainly line-of-sight and a bit beyond. Buildings and trees are ignored in that statement but they do have an effect. A roof mounted antenna, getting above the local clutter and offering a clear path is most effective and better than increasing the transmit power. It is equally effective on receive. Ranges of many tens of kilometres are achievable under those circumstances, depending on terrain. With a handheld device amongst building clutter distances will be much reduced. Repeaters, mounted on hilltops, allow extended range to handheld and mobile users. As the frequency increases the ranges tend to reduce and so does building penetration unless you happen to be next to a window on the transmitter side of the building.

Sample Questions

There are only two propagation questions for Foundation candidates, as the table shows.

Question	Syllabus Item
17	6a.1, 6a.2, 6a.3, 6a.4, 6a.5
18	6b.1, 6b.2

f6a1-1

One feature of radio waves is that they
A find it easier to go straight through buildings and hills to give a good signal on the far side
B travel in straight lines unless they bounce of a surface, are bent in the ionosphere or diffract round hills
C curve round obstructions such as hills so as to fill in all the space on the far side
D stop as soon as they reach a building, tree or hill.

f6a2-1

The drawing shows a transmitter on a hill covering the flat ground to the right. When travelling from point A to B the VHF signal is expected to
A remain constant all the time the transmitter is in clear view
B vary up and down every wavelength of the signal
C steadily decrease all the way to B
D be quite weak at A but increase to a steady signal once away from the effect of the hill.

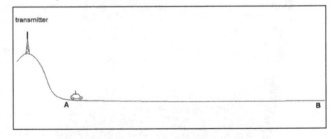

f6a3-1

The drawing shows a transmitter with a hill between it and the receiver. When travelling from point A to B the VHF signal is expected to
A remain constant all the time
B be quite weak at A but increase once away from the hill
C vary up and down every wavelength of the signal
D be receivable at A but get progressively weaker.

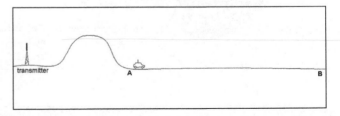

f6a4-1

Which action is likely to result in the best performance on transmit and receive?

A   Fixing the antenna on a short pole in the garden.
B   Mounting the antenna above the chimney on the house.
C   Hanging the antenna in the loft.
D   Using a power amplifier to boost the transmitted signal.

f6a5-1

An amateur has the choice of VHF or UHF for a particular contact of some 25km. Which statement below best describes his choice?

A   If the VHF and UHF antennas are the same and side-by-side then there will be no difference in performance.
B   The UHF option is most likely to give a better signal.
C   The VHF option is most likely to give a better signal.
D   The choice will depend on the time of day or night.

f6b1-1

Which statement best describes the ionosphere?

A   The ionosphere is a region of refractive gasses 70 to 400km in altitude.
B   The ionosphere is a reflective surface at the top of the atmosphere.
C   The ionosphere appears only during the night.
D   The ionosphere appears only during the day.

f6b2-1

Which factor does NOT affect propagation in the ionosphere?

A   The radio frequency.
B   The time of year.
C   The time of day.
D   The day of the week.

INTERMEDIATE

The ionosphere

At Foundation we learnt that the ionosphere extends from 70 to 400km. It is also divided up into layers. The lowest is the D layer at 70km, then the E layer at 120km and finally the F1 and F2 layers at 300 and 400km. The UV light from the sun causes the ionisation so the F2 layer, being the highest, is the most highly ionised. Much of the UV has been absorbed by the time it reaches the D layer so the ionisation is weaker. Charged particles from the sun also have an effect and this varies over the 11-year sunspot cycle as well as the daily and seasonal changes. The sunspot number gives the level of solar activity and a higher number means higher ionisation and better HF propagation.

Being the most highly ionised the F2 layer is the main mode of ionospheric propagation. Since the air is rarefied at that altitude, recombination or natural de-ionisation is slow and the F2 layer remains ionised (but weaker) all night.

Ground wave and skip

There are three main modes of propagation. Ionospheric or sky wave, ground wave and tropospheric wave, sometimes called the (free) space wave. The troposphere is the region below the ionosphere and above the direct effect of the ground. It is relevant to VHF, UHF and microwave propagation.

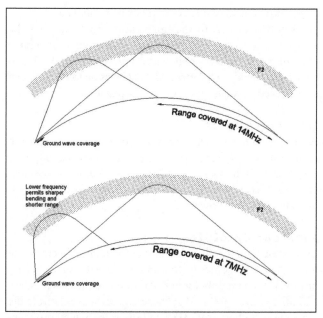

Fig 6.1. HF waves are refracted back to earth by the ionosphere. Lower frequencies can be bent more and returned closer to the transmitter.

The ground wave is a ground-hugging wave whose range is very frequency dependent. At domestic 'long wave' frequencies and below, below about 200kHz, ground wave range is many hundreds or thousands of km with the lowest frequencies allowing global coverage. However, even by 'top band', 1·8MHz, the range is severely reduced to a few tens of kilometres over good ground or sea and to just a few kilometres at 3·5MHz.

The amount of bending in the ionosphere depends on the level of ionisation and the frequency. Higher frequencies are harder to bend and require higher ionisation, which occurs during the day. A longer path requires less bending, whereas a short one will need the wave to be bent through almost 180°. This is illustrated in **Fig 6.1**. The lower frequency wave can be returned to earth closer to the transmitter.

The skip distance is the distance from the transmitter to the closest point of return of the sky wave. It is shorter for lower frequencies. The skip or dead zone is a ring round the transmitter bounded by the fading out of the ground wave and the closest point of return of the sky wave. No signal is heard in the skip zone.

Tropospheric Propagation

The troposphere is the region below the ionosphere and above the direct influence of the ground. Under normal atmospheric conditions, the water vapour and air pressure changes with height have a small refractive effect. Radio waves curve downwards slightly, but not as much as the curvature of the earth. That allows communication a bit beyond what would otherwise be regarded as line of sight.

'Lift' and Sporadic-E

"There's a lift on" is amateur parlance for enhanced propagation. On 2m and 70cm it is often because there is a *duct*. When there is high pressure or the temperature drops suddenly, layers of air can be formed which trap the radio wave, curving it back into the layer, so it only spreads out horizontally. These layers are called ducts. They allow the wave to travel very much further, achieving several times its normal range.

Another effect, in the upper atmosphere, is that the E layer, which only weakly refracts radio signals, can have random regions of very high ionisation, permitting VHF and even UHF signals to be refracted. Distances up to 2000km can be achieved by such 'Sporadic-E' propagation.

Weather effects

As the frequencies rise, heavy rain, snow and ice can absorb sufficient energy from the wave to cause attenuation. This can affect UHF frequencies and above. At microwave frequencies, signals can be lost entirely for brief periods, often affecting satellite TV reception.

Amateur Satellites

Low earth orbit satellites are below the higher layers of the ionosphere and some do transmit in the HF band. Mostly however, and certainly for high altitude satellites, VHF, UHF and microwaves are used as those signals will penetrate the ionosphere. Otherwise VHF and higher frequency propagation is all conducted in the troposphere, essentially on a line-of-sight basis.

Frequency and wavelength

At Foundation level a graph was used to convert frequency and wavelength. It may have been noted that the frequency in MHz, multiplied by the wavelength, λ, in metres, always came to about 300. This is because the velocity of light and of radio waves in free space and air is 3×10^8 m/s and a wavelength is the distance travelled in the time for 1 cycle. The formula is

$$v = f\lambda$$

where v is the velocity 300,000,000 metres per second, f is the frequency in Hz and λ the wavelength in metres.

Sample Questions

At this level we have three questions to consider, drawn from syllabus areas:

Question	Syllabus Item
28	6a.1 6a.2 6a.3 6a.4
29	6a.5 6a.6 6a.7
30	6a.8

i6a1-1

The lowest layer of the ionosphere is the

A   E-layer

B   F1 layer

C   F2 layer

D   D layer.

i6a2-1

HF propagation is found to vary over a number of years. This is because

A   natural phenomena always vary, there need be no specific reason

B   the number of sunspots varies in a cyclic manner

C   the jet stream affects the level of ionisation

D   the gulf stream affects air temperatures, which in turn affect the ionosphere.

i6a3-1

Most HF propagation occurs by

A   ground wave

B   E-layer refraction

C   F-layer refraction

D   tropospheric waves.

i6a4-1

When listening to a conversation on HF it is noticed that an Italian station is strong but the UK station, which is much closer, is barely audible at all. A likely reason for this is that

A   the Italian station is running more power

B   the UK station is using a large Yagi antenna and beaming away from you

C   sporadic-E is wiping out the UK station's signal

D   you are in the skip zone of the UK station but not the Italian one.

i6a5-1

Sporadic-E is often responsible for

A   VHF signals received at much greater ranges than usual

B   a sudden loss of HF propagation lasting a few hours

C   a larger number of sunspots than usual

D   ducting in the troposphere.

i6a6-1

Which frequencies normally pass through the ionosphere?

A   Lower HF signals.

B   HF and VHF signals.

C   VHF and higher signals.

D   Only UHF and microwave signals.

i6a7-1

Which statement about propagation is correct?

A   The HF band suffers attenuation from heavy rain, especially in the winter.

B   Attenuation due to snow and ice affects UHF and higher frequency signals.

C   VHF signals are absorbed by falling snow but higher frequencies have shorter wavelengths and can pass between the individual flakes.

D   The attenuation of radio signals is largely independent of frequency but is affected by rainfall intensity.

i6a8-1

The 10GHz amateur band extends from10·00GHz to 10·50GHz. The wavelengths are of the order of

A   3m

B   30cm

C   3cm

D   3mm.

E-M waves

Fig 6.2 shows an electromagnetic wave the E component (electric) and H component (magnetic) are in phase but the planes of oscillation are at right angles and also at right angles to the direction of propagation. The E field defines the polarisation.

If an RF signal is applied to two dipoles set at right-angles and the signal to one delayed by $\lambda/4$ by an extra length of coaxial feeder, then the radiated signal will rotate, that is, the plane of the E and H vectors will rotate about the direction of propagation, one rotation per wavelength. A helical antenna will achieve the same effect. That is circular polarisation. The two directions of rotation, right-handed (clockwise seen from behind) and left-handed are orthogonal; a right-handed antenna will not respond to a left-handed signal. Circular polarisation is useful for satellite communication, where the orientation of the satellite is indeterminate.

Spreading loss

As the signal spreads out the signal covers a larger area and gets weaker. At double the distance the signal power is one quarter of its previous level. That is known as the Inverse Square Law. Note it is the power, or rather the Power Flux Density (PFD) in w/m², that obeys this rule. The Field Strength in V/m is a linear reciprocal relationship, the field strength is halved when doubling the distance.

Ionosphere

The level of ionisation is a balance between the rate of production of ionisation by UV light and charged solar particles and the ongoing recombination. The F2 layer at 300 - 400km is the most rarefied and the most irradiated and has the highest level of ionisation. It can refract the highest HF frequencies and is the main mode of propagation. The geometry is such that a single hop can reach 4000km.

The F1 layer is less highly ionised but may refract lower frequencies. After dark the F1 and F2 layers merge but the F layer remains ionised all night.

The E layer at 120km is denser and partly protected by the layers above. It is less highly ionised and the ionisation falls not long after sunset. During the day it can refract lower frequencies but randomly occurring very highly ionised regions, Sporadic-E, can refract into the VHF and occasionally UHF bands.

The D layer is the most weakly ionised and disappears at dusk. It does not normally refract radio waves but does ab-

sorb their energy, attenuating the wave. It is that attenuation which prevents distant medium wave broadcasts being heard during the say. The signals never reach the F2 layer.

MUF, LUF and fading

The MUF, maximum usable frequency, depends on the degree of ionisation, the frequency and the length of path over which it is desired to operate. A long path requires less bending in the ionosphere as already shown in Fig 6.1.

The LUF, lowest usable frequency is set by D layer absorption. Signals of lower frequency are attenuated in the D layer. It is possible for the LUF to be higher than the MUF so no propagation is possible. This is more likely to occur when the path is from day to night where the night MUF is low but further along the path the LUF is high.

Fig 6.3 shows how the MUF and LUF vary over the 24-hour cycle and from summer to winter. The path is from the UK to the E coast USA and note the refraction points are mid-path and it is the local time there that determines the MUF. The time offset and longer summer day is clearly visible in the LUF graph, remembering the D-layer relies on a visible sun.

Ionospheric refraction depends on the level of ionisation, which undergoes small random variations. Consequently there are a number of parallel paths from transmitter to receiver all with slightly different path lengths. The received signal is the sum of all these individual signals, which will have random phase offsets. Sometimes these will add to a very strong signal and other times they can cancel out. The received signal varies both in slow time over a few tens of seconds and quickly over a second or two. This is slow and fast fading. The receiver AGC will avoid dramatic volume changes but there may well be times of inadequate signal. Operating just below the MUF can reduce the number of parallel paths and the incidence of fading. Many authorities refer to an optimum work-

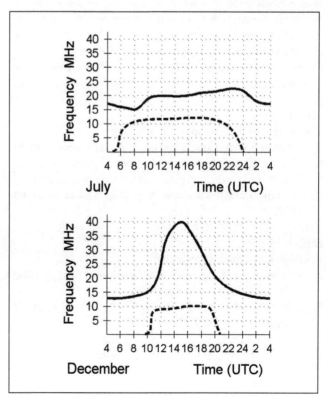

Fig 6.3. Variation of the MUF and LUF over the 24 hour cycle. The range of MUF is much greater in the winter.

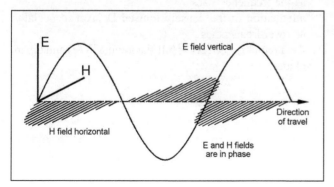

Fig 6.2. The electromagnetic wave.

ing frequency about 15% below the MUF.

The Critical Frequency of Vertical Incidence, usually simply termed the critical frequency, is the highest frequency that will be returned to earth on a vertical path. From that the MUF on any path can be estimated provided the mid-point of that path is not too far from the location where the critical frequency was measured. The critical frequency requires a 180° refraction and is always lower than the MUF. On a long path the MUF can be up to five times the critical frequency.

Sample Questions

There are three questions on propagation in the Advanced paper.

Question	Syllabus Item
41	6a.1, 6a.2
42	6b.1, 6b.2, 6b.3, 6b.4
43	6b.5, 6b.6, 6b.7, 6c.1

a6a1-1
Circular polarisation is characterised by the electric and magnetic
A   vectors rotating in opposite directions
B   vectors having a 90° phase difference, giving the appearance of rotation
C   fields taking the form of closed circles rather than a flat plane of polarisation
D   fields remaining at right angles but rotating through one revolution per wavelength.

a6a2-1
In an e-m wave the
A   field strength falls linearly with distance
B   field strength obeys the inverse square law with distance
C   power flux density drops linearly with distance
D   power flux density depends on the square root of the field strength.

a6b1-1
The D layer of the ionosphere is at a height of
A   70km and allows single hop propagation of about 140km
B   70km and tends to prevent ionospheric propagation
C   120km and tends to prevent ionospheric propagation
D   250km and allows single hop propagation of about 2000km.

a6b2-1
Sporadic E is a phenomenon that
A   can cause a fade out of ionospheric propagation following major sunspot activity
B   can refract VHF and UHF signals back to the earth's surface
C   traps HF signals in an ionospheric duct
D   scatters HF signals in random directions.

a6b3-1
Assuming the path London to Sydney is 17000km, the most likely path for a HF contact between the two cities is by
A   four ionospheric hops, refracting in the F2 layer
B   five ionospheric hops, refracting in the F2 layer
C   five ionospheric hops, refracting in the F1 layer
D   four ionospheric hops, refracting in the F1 layer.

a6b4-1
Fading is normally caused by
A   variations in the MUF affecting propagation of signals too close in frequency
B   mutual interference between ground wave and sky wave paths
C   phase differences between mostly parallel sky wave paths
D   absorption in the D layer attenuating the signals.

a6b5-1
The highest MUFs can be expected to occur during the
A   day in the winter
B   night in the winter
C   day in the summer
D   night in the summer.

a6b6-1
It is normally found that continental medium wave broadcast stations are heard during the night in the UK, but not during the day. The reason for this is that
A   few continental stations broadcast during the day
B   the MUF is too high for medium wave signals to be refracted
C   the F1 and F2 layers are separated during the day but combine at night
D   the D layer will absorb medium wave signals during the day but is absent at night.

a6b7-1
A contact between central Russia and the UK in the winter is
A   most likely on 3·5MHz in the mornings
B   most likely on 21MHz in the mornings
C   more likely on 21MHz than 3·5MHz in the afternoons
D   unlikely on 3·5MHz in the evenings.

a6c1-1
HF ground wave range is limited by
A   energy absorption in the ground, which is more significant as the frequency rises
B   energy absorption in the ground, which is less significant as the frequency rises
C   attenuation in the densely ionised D layer, especially at lower frequencies
D   the attenuating effects of hill shadowing, trees and urban clutter.

7. EMC

The aim of electromagnetic compatibility (EMC) is the avoidance of interference between different pieces of electronic equipment. Unfortunately, transmitters are designed to radiate and may be the source of interference. All radio receivers are designed to receive weak signals and are more likely to suffer from interference, which can come from other transmitters or other sources such as a sparking electrical contact, electric motor, thermostat and fluorescent or electronic lighting.

Routes of interference

The interference can get from the source to the victim device by various ways. An amateur transmitter will radiate RF from its antenna, but it may also have unintended radiation from the feeder from the transmitter to the antenna and may allow some RF to escape down the power leads and mains. Those leads will be closer to or even connected to the victim device. Conducted interference may occur where there is a copper path all the way from the transmitter to the victim device.

Radiated pickup can be 'direct', that is it directly enters the wiring inside the victim device. This occurs mainly at VHF and UHF where the device may have internal wiring around $\lambda/4$ long. Such interference is normally independent of the exact frequency. Radiated RF can also be picked up by power leads, audio leads, loudspeaker leads, telephone lines and computer data lines. It can then be conducted into the victim device.

RF conducted out of the transmitter can be minimised by filters and ferrite rings on its power leads and its power supply (if separate), and by the provision of an RF earth so any RF does have somewhere to safely go. To minimise the radiated signal being picked up by other wiring, the antenna should be as far away as possible from the houses so the strength of the signal has dropped by being spread out more. Most domestic houses are more susceptible to vertical fields so, at HF, a balanced horizontal antenna is likely to be the best option from an EMC viewpoint. End-fed antenna when fed from the house end, have high currents and voltages close to the house and should be avoided.

Vertical antennas are typically more of a problem, but with limited space the benefit of being smaller and able to be sited further away may turn out better than a horizontal antenna where one end is close to the house.

The leads into a victim device can be filtered, typically ferrite rings, so any RF that is picked up is filtered out to minimise entry and interference.

Experienced amateurs, the local amateur club and the RSGB EMC committee are able to assist with advice and the EMC committee web site has several advisory leaflets.

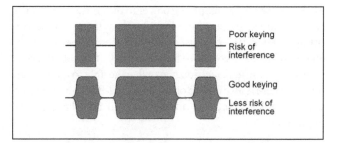

Fig 7.1. Rounded edges to Morse keying reduce the risk of key clicks and interference.

Power and mode

The more power a station runs, the more likely is the interference. At the Foundation limit of 10W problems are not that likely. This may change when the same antenna is later used at the 50W limit of the Intermediate licence.

Most problems are caused by amplitude changes so SSB and AM are potential problems. FM has a constant amplitude and is much less likely to cause problems. Many data systems have a constant amplitude so are also quite good. CW problems depend on the way the Morse is keyed. Fast on / off edges as shown in **Fig 7.1** are likely to cause problems but rounded edges can be almost as good, that is, as interference free, as FM.

Immunity

It is an obligation on amateurs to do all they can to ensure their station is as good as it can be, especially minimising the risk of causing interference. Nonetheless, some reliance is also placed on the ability of potential victim equipment to withstand modest interference. That is its *immunity*. Fitting external chokes such as ferrite rings and filters can improve the immunity. Conducted interference can and should be cured at the transmitter, but mains and antenna leads can pick up transmitted signals and route then into the affected device. The ferrite ring or filter should be as close to the device as possible, leaving little unprotected lead to pick up the RF.

Only ready made filters should be fitted; home made devices in mains leads should not be considered at Foundation level. That is for properly qualified persons only. Snap-on ferrite rings are available for occasions where plugs are moulded on, preventing threading the cable through ferrite rings. The RSGB and amateur radio suppliers should be consulted regarding suitable devices. Surge suppressors are available from computer suppliers and can do that task well but they are not suitable as RF filters. Ferrite rings for computer protection may be less effective for RF.

RF earths

The RF earth is to provide a safe path for unwanted RF currents, which would otherwise flow back along the mains wiring and cause problems. It comprises a substantial copper rod, often steel cored, hammered into the ground, away from buried cables, pipes and other services, and connected to the transmitter by a short and substantial lead or braid. Ferrite rings on the mains safety earth will also help prevent RF into the mains. **Under NO circumstances should the mains safety earth be disconnected.**

PME - Protective Multiple Earth

PME is a method of supplying power to the house. The details are beyond the scope of the Foundation syllabus but before fitting an RF earth you must check with the electricity supply company to see if you have a PME supply. The supply company or a qualified electrician may then be able to advise you further. There is also advice on the RSGB EMC committee web site. Do not neglect this precaution as it may have safety implications.

The neighbours

The licence states that you must not "cause Undue Interference to any wireless telegraphy". For the purpose of the licence conditions questions in the exam, that is the correct answer. In reality, you should seek not to cause any interference to any electrical equipment, even non-radio devices. If interference is caused to the neighbours they will regard it as your fault, even though you are licensed and taking great care. It may very well be that their equipment has poor immunity or is badly installed. Despite that, you should stop doing whatever is causing the problem and try to cure it. Whatever the real merits of the situation, you do need to live with your neighbours. They don't want to limit your hobby, simply enjoy their own activities, including watching TV.

Ask if you can carry out tests at a suitable time to determine the cause of the problem. You may need experienced help, both in solving the problem and in presenting an impartial face to the neighbours. Be sure it *is* impartial, or both of you will lose credibility.

The RSGB EMC committee can help with telephoned advice (for RSGB members) and their web site has many leaflets offering advice. As a last resort Ofcom can be called in if the interference is to radio and TV equipment. A fee may be charged and your station will be inspected. The odds are that you will get a clean bill of health if you have followed the advice and it is much better if the Ofcom officer tells the neighbours and then helps solve the actual problem.

Sample Questions

Three questions are asked on this important topic.

Question	Syllabus Item
19	7a.1, 7a.2, 7a.3, 7a.4
20	7b.1, 7b.2
21	7c.1, 7c.2, 7c.3, 7d.1

f7a1-1
Good EMC practice is
A the avoidance of interference between electronic devices
B installing external antennas so they are not seen by the neighbours
C ensuring every transmission from the station is carefully logged
D not transmitting when the neighbours are likely to be watching TV.

f7a2-1
Interference to other electronic equipment is most likely to be caused by
A a soldering iron
B a digital electric clock
C a fixed telephone
D an amateur transmitter.

f7a3-1
A domestic radio receiver is suffering interference, even when the amateur next door is away. The interference could be caused by
A a rechargeable razor
B an electric drill
C a steam iron
D a radio controlled clock.

f7a4-1
The drawing shows a music system in a house. It is suffering from interference and some protective measures have already been taken but with little effect. Where might the interference be getting in?
A Via the remote control.
B Conducted along the power leads from the transmitter.
C Picked up on the loudspeaker leads.
D Picked up on the mains lead.

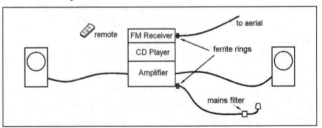

f7b1-1
If all other factors are equal, which HF antenna is the LEAST likely to cause interference problems?
A A vertical antenna at the far end of the garden.
B A balanced horizontal antenna at the far end of the garden.
C A vertical antenna on the roof.
D A balanced horizontal antenna in the loft.

f7b2-1
Which transmission is the MOST likely to cause interference?
A 2W of SSB.
B 10W of SSB.
C 2W of FM.
D 10W of FM.

f7c1-1

When fitting ferrite rings on the TV down lead from its aerial, the ferrite ring should be fitted

A as close to the wall outlet as possible

B in the middle of the lead from the wall to the TV

C a quarter of a wavelength from the TV

D as close to the TV as possible.

f7c2-1

It is decided that a suitable filter is needed on the mains lead to the TV to prevent interference from an amateur transmitter in the same house. A good solution is to

A obtain a surge suppressor from the local computer supplies shop

B make a suitable filter from a design seen in a book

C buy a filter from an amateur radio dealer

D write to the local authority and ask their advice.

f7c3-1

When fitting an RF earth it may also be helpful to

A disconnect the mains earth wire in the plug

B fit a ferrite ring on the mains lead

C fit a ferrite ring on the RF earth lead

D disconnect the outer braid of the antenna feeder.

f7d1-1

If a neighbour complains of interference to his television, you should

A show him your licence to prove you are allowed to transmit

B say it cannot be you as you are only transmitting voice, not pictures

C stop and ask if you can carry out a test to see what is causing the problem

D accept that it might not be possible to practice amateur radio in that neighbourhood.

INTERMEDIATE

One of the basic principles of electromagnetic compatibility is that equipment should be able to function satisfactorily in its electromagnetic environment and without causing intolerable electromagnetic disturbance to other apparatus in that environment. Put simply, electrical equipment should not cause problems and be reasonably immune to being affected.

That principle will avoid interference, but a transmitter is intended to produce radio signals, and receivers are supposed to pick them up. A transmitter in a built-up area is at risk of causing problems, especially to radio receivers trying to pick up signals on other frequencies. It is necessary to install transmitters and their antennas carefully to avoid or at least minimise the risk and be prepared to take further steps if a problem does occur.

The European EMC Directive enforces the basic principle, and electronic equipment produced since the mid 1990s should be much less likely to suffer from radio interference.

Good housekeeping

Power supplies should be filtered, mains safety earths properly connected and all connections, mains, DC power, audio and RF must use good quality cables and plugs designed for that purpose. Screened and coaxial cables must have their outer braid properly connected to the metallic shell of plugs and sockets so the screen is continuous.

Take care to route mains cables in one direction and RF cables in another to keep them well separated. Similarly the RF feeders should be well away from other radio and TV leads.

At HF an RF earth is probably essential and may well be needed at VHF too. It consists of a substantial earth rod hammered a good 1· 5m into the ground, avoiding buried pipes and cables and kept moist. It is connected by a short fat lead or braid to the main earth point on the transmitter or ATU, or both.

Fig 7.2 shows why an RF earth is needed and the cause of the RF earth currents. In (A) the antenna is well balanced and the current in one leg of the antenna is equal and opposite the current in the other. There is no residual RF to flow to earth. In (B) which may represent an end-fed or vertical antenna there is an RF current in the antenna but nowhere to complete the circuit. Consequently the circuit is completed using the mains earth and as much RF may flow there as in the antenna. In (C) an RF earth is provided to take that current and ferrite rings (possibly several) on the mains lead dissuades RF in the mains. Such 'single ended' antennas are often said to be tuned (or fed) against earth.

The comments about PME in the Foundation section should be re-read.

Antennas should be well away from mains wiring, TV and radio feeders, phone lines and houses generally. Loft mounted antennas are particularly prone to cause interference, especially if the TV aerial is beside it!

Fig 7.3 shows a station layout that should minimise the risk of EMC problems.

Filters

A filter is a device that permits some frequencies to pass readily but blocks others. By this means DC power and 50Hz AC power can pass but RF, particularly RF interference can be blocked. A ferrite ring acts as a type of filter and provides attenuation of unwanted RF. Typically a mains lead may be wound four or five times through such a ring. These are fitted close to the transmitter so the lead does not radiate RF as well as blocking conducted RF.

There are four basic types of

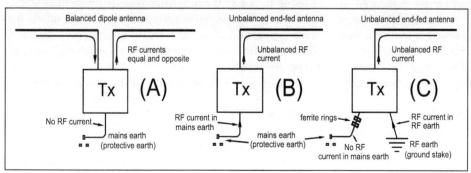

Fig 7.2. The cause of RF earth currents.

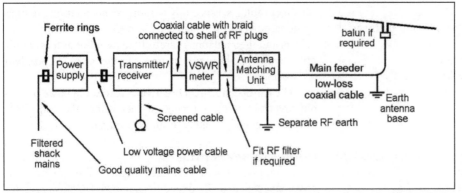

Fig 7.3. The layout of a station with good EMC characteristics, provided the power is controlled.

filter: low pass, eg the mains filter just mentioned; high pass, passes high frequencies and blocks low ones; band pass, only permits a small range of frequencies to pass; and band stop, which blocks a small range of frequencies. Their frequency / pass characteristics were shown in Fig 4.7.

The TV broadcast band is 470 - 854MHz so to protect against HF and VHF signals, a high-pass filter needs to be fitted in the TV down lead.

Checking your station

Following the above housekeeping advice is likely to avoid most problems, but we must still check.

A general coverage receiver will be good for this but some care is needed to avoid getting misleading results. Placing the receiver next to a transmitter will probably overload the receiver, causing harmonics and other effects, which appear as real signals but exist only inside the receiver. The solution is to move the receiver away until the wanted signal is not overloading and the signal strength meter is indicating below full scale. Now sweeping the receiver slowly across the bands will identify any harmonics, which you can calculate in advance, and spurious signals.

Don't forget to identify yourself since this is a radiating test, and do choose a quiet time and frequency. Log keeping is not compulsory but you are strongly advised to keep a log of these checks; it will show you are taking interference issues seriously.

Interference effects to Radio and TV

Analogue TV is affected in different ways depending on the nature of the modulation of the interfering signal. Although many households will invest in digital TVs, it is likely that others will retain their analogue TV as long as it is serviceable, using a digital set-top box.

FM transmissions cause a diagonal wavy patterning on the picture often called a herringbone pattern, possible loss or change of colour and less often the sound is muffled. SSB causes the picture to jump, pattern or break up in time with speech. The sound may be affected but since TV sound is frequency modulated, there is unlikely to be anything recognisable.

Sparking from motors in electric drills, lawn mowers, food processors etc can cause spots on the screen and possibly clicks on sound. Thermostats can make quite an intense buzz and burst of heavy interference of a second or two as they switch, repeated a few minutes later.

Digital TV

Digital TV is quite different. The transmission is a data stream of binary 0s and 1s together with error protection coding that can allow data recovery from a modest number of data bits received erroneously. Weak signals and interference all contribute to impairment in the bit error ratio. When this ratio is too great, ie too many errors to recover the correct data, the system fails. Picture coding is such that larger blocks are defined first and subsequent data fills in the block detail. In addition, to reduce the data rate, much of the next frame is simply sent as the detail that has changed. If the camera has panned across, for example, then all that needs to be sent is an instruction to move everything two pixels to the right and the new two pixel columns, plus any actual movement in the picture detail. When too many errors occur the picture may freeze because the update information is not available or become jerky when only some updates are received. The picture may pixellate into larger blocks, a bit like a jigsaw; or it may collapse entirely and blank out. Some of these effects are viewable now on analogue TVs showing pictures from moving outside broadcast cameras because the video link is digital.

It is not possible to identify the cause of the problem; weak signals and different types of interference all have much the same effect.

Masthead and TV amplifiers

These can be bad news for two reasons. Many of them are designed for a pan-European market and cover a very wide range of frequencies that can include the 2m and 70cm bands, the TV bands and the VHF / FM broadcast band all in one go. They also suggest that TV signals may be low in that area, making it more likely that even modest interference will cause problems. Ideally, if an amplifier is needed at all, it should be a high quality, filtered masthead type. Any additional filters should be fitted at the amplifier input rather than the TV input. With a masthead type and a long down lead, an additional filter at the TV may also be required.

Being wideband and covering amateur frequencies makes such amplifiers more susceptible to overloading. Malfunction can affect the way it handles the TV signal even if the TV was able to cope with the interference. It is also possible that the extra amplification will then overload the TV. Step 1 in such cases is to see if the amplifier is actually needed at all, although in weak signal areas it probably will be unless the aerial is poor and of low gain. A better aerial may then be a solution, particularly if it is not pointing towards the source of the interference.

If overloading is suspected, transmitting into a dummy load will show if the signal is leaking out elsewhere. If it is the filtering at the transmitter power leads needs some attention.

Medium wave radio

Medium wave radio is much more susceptible to interference since the medium wave broadcasts use amplitude modulation and most interference effects are amplitude related. Electric motors may produce a growl related to motor speed, the switching of fluorescent lights may be heard as clicks as the tube strikes and dimmers may cause a continuous buzz related to the brilliance. FM can cause muffled sound or loss of sound and SSB can be partially demodulated into an unintelligible or sometimes intelligible speech like sound.

Computers can emit a continuous buzz on several frequencies, mainly harmonics of the clock and other internal signals. For this and most of the above situations the distance to the source can be critical and further separation may solve the problem.

Mains filters (of proper commercial origin) RF filters and ferrite rings will improve the immunity but ideally interference should be dealt with at source so the interference does not affect other equipments and the neighbours. In fitting filters, it is necessary to consider the frequency of the interference and the frequencies the device is intended to receive. The right type of filter, high, low pass etc, can then be chosen.

Log keeping

Log keeping is no longer compulsory; it was prior to 2007. Nonetheless, it will show what you were doing if a complaint does occur. A well kept and up to date log will also go a long way to showing the authorities that you were not operating at that time. Without the log, you are on your own. It also helps if the complainant keeps a log, that is likely to be asked of him or her if a formal complaint is made, so it helps all round if both parties keep logs.

Conducting tests will be easier with a log, you have a head start on what to look for. Do try very hard to get the neighbour to co-operate with this and co-operate yourself in avoiding TV viewing hours.

As said in the Foundation guide, the RSGB EMC committee produce leaflets aimed at both you and at the neighbour.

Sample Questions

At Intermediate level there are five EMC questions.

Question	Syllabus Item
31	7a.1 7a.2 7a.3
32	7b.1 7b.2 7b.3 7b.4 7b.5
33	7c.1 7c.2 7c.3
34	7c.4 7c.5 7c.6
35	7d.1 7d.2 7d.3

i7a1-1

Which statement below BEST describes the concept of electromagnetic compatibility?
A Electronic equipments must avoid causing any electromagnetic disturbance.
B Electronic equipments must be immune to ill effects due to electromagnetic disturbance.
C Equipments must be reasonably immune to electromagnetic disturbance and must not cause intolerable disturbance.
D Equipments that do not adequately limit the electromagnetic disturbance they cause or are insufficiently immune must be marked as not complying.

i7a2-1

An amateur radio transmitter
A is licensed to cause electromagnetic disturbance to other electronic equipment
B might cause RF fields stronger than the agreed limits on electromagnetic disturbance
C must not be able to cause electromagnetic disturbance to any electronic equipment
D must be certified as being capable of causing electromagnetic disturbance.

i7a3-1

New electronic equipment should meet the European EMC immunity requirements
A and older equipments must be brought up to the current agreed standards
B but older or poorly installed equipments might not meet the agreed standards
C and existing installations must be re-tested to the new agreed standards
D and must avoid causing difficulties to older equipments not meeting the standards.

i7b1-1

The connection between a transmitter and an antenna tuning unit
A should be made using coaxial cable and RF plugs which connect with the braid
B can use any type of cable since the antenna tuning unit will avoid any problems
C should not be longer that one quarter of a wavelength to avoid matching problems
D must include a suitable balun for the frequencies in use by the transmitter.

i7b2-1

The purpose of a filter in the power supply leads to a transceiver is to
A prevent noise and interference on the mains from affecting the receiver
B minimise the production of harmonics, which may cause interference
C minimise the level of RF from the transmitter getting into the mains wiring
D ensure the supply to the transceiver is properly balanced.

i7b3-1

A good RF earth
A should be used in place of the house mains earth
B is the house mains water supply pipe
C is a short fat lead to copper rods buried in the garden
D is only required for frequencies above 430MHz.

i7b4-1

Checking for spurious signals and harmonics from the transmitter is best done using
A a wavemeter, that is a tuneable diode receiver
B a general coverage receiver
C a frequency counter
D an RF power meter.

i7b5-1

Using a loft antenna for amateur radio activities is

A normally quite satisfactory if an outside antenna will look unsightly

B likely to cause considerable interference to TV reception

C only advisable for frequencies above 30MHz

D only advisable for frequencies below 30MHz.

i7c1-1

A digital TV is suffering from modest interference from an FM amateur transmission. This may be seen as

A a jerky picture and jigsaw like pixellation

B loss of colour and a severe buzz on sound

C wavy lines and patterning on the picture

D spots on the screen and possible clicks on sound.

i7c2-1

A TV is suffering every few minutes from a short burst of heavy interference causing many horizontal streaks on the picture and a rasping sound. A likely source is

A a nearby computer

B an amateur transmitter

C a thermostat

D a fluorescent light.

i7c3-1

A domestic radio is found to be susceptible to interference from an amateur transmission. Tuning the radio to different frequencies has little effect and asking the amateur to transmit in other parts of the band has little effect either. Ferrite rings on the transmitter power leads made no difference. It is likely the receiver is suffering from

A direct pickup

B conducted interference

C a poor earth connection

D an almost flat battery.

i7c4-1

A known problem with many masthead TV amplifiers is that

A they are tuned only to the UK TV channels

B they amplify a wide range of frequencies

C their power supply is often delivered via the coaxial down lead

D linear amplifiers are commonly used.

i7c5-1

HF and VHF transmissions occasionally cause interference to a nearby TV set. A possible cure is to fit a

A low pass filter in the TV aerial down lead

B high pass filter in the TV aerial down lead

C low pass filter in the transmitter feeder

D high pass filter in the transmitter feeder.

i7c6-1

Fitting ferrite rings on the aerial lead to the amateur's own television has failed to cure a case of interference. It is now suspected the signal is either being conducted from the transmitter power leads to the TV or the transmitted signal is being picked up by the mains wiring to the TV. To determine which it is, a suitable test would be to fit a

A ferrite ring on the transmitter feeder

B ferrite ring on the TV mains lead

C low pass filter on the transmitter output

D dummy load on the transmitter output.

i7d1-1

A good reason for keeping a station log is that

A you can check if you were or were not transmitting at a time interference was complained of

B it will remind you when you need to revalidate your amateur licence

C you will know how many hours your transmitter has been used if a warranty repair is needed

D will be able to make a note of names of the people you have contacted.

i7d2-1

A neighbour approaches you with a record of times over the last two weeks when he was suffering from interference. You should

A send this record to Ofcom with a request for investigation

B compare the times of interference with your station log

C advise him to show this to his TV service engineer

D ask him to continue recording for another two weeks.

i7d3-1

Information leaflets on dealing with cases of interference are available from

A television service engineers

B the RSGB EMC committee

C the reference section of a local library

D most TV and electronic shops.

ADVANCED

A key requirement in understanding how unwanted signals may enter other electronic systems is knowing how they function and their weaknesses.

The TV broadcast band extends from 470MHz to 854MHz, TV IFs are in the range 33 - 40MHz and the video baseband is 0 - 5MHz with the colour sub-carrier at 4·43MHz.

The radio FM broadcast band, Band 2, is 87·5 - 108MHz and radio IFs are typically 10·7MHz. The medium wave extends from 526·5kHz to 1606·5kHz and those IFs are typically in the range 455 - 470kHz.

Chapter 4 noted that the image channel of a receiver was on the opposite side of the LO to the wanted signal. At medium wave the LO is usually above the wanted signal to reduce its percentage tuning range and that puts the images in the 1·8MHz amateur band. Images and IFs are frequencies at which radio receivers can be expected to be less immune to the effects of unwanted signals.

Blocking, de-sensing, cross-modulation and intermodulation

Receiver front ends are often quite wide, selectivity is achieved in the IF stages. Strong amateur transmissions can enter the RF and mixer stages and cause an overload. The behaviour of those stages can be disrupted (blocking), impaired (de-sensing) or affected in time with the modulation on the amateur signal. The wanted signal now contains effects related to the amateur modulation, which may be intelligible. This is known as cross-modulation. Since masthead amplifiers are frequently very wide-band devices, they are particularly prone to this type of interference. A front-end filter or a properly filtered amplifier can often cure the problem.

Another effect is intermodulation (see Chapter 4 Advanced). Two strong signals may combine to produce unintended sum and difference signals or other multiples such as twice one frequency minus the other. These intermodulation products (imps) may fall on or close to the wanted signal, causing interference. These spurious signals are generated inside the victim receiver; they do not exist outside and are no reflection on the transmission. The two signals are simply too strong for the victim receiver to cope with. Amateur receivers allow for this possibility by providing a switchable attenuator at the front end, removing the overload and thus removing the imps.

Passive intermodulation occurs outside the victim receiver and can be heard on any receiver. It normally requires a very strong signal and is the classic 'rusty bolt effect'. A corroded contact creates a non-linear or rectifying junction and that gives rise to the intermodulation products. The corroded contact may be in the transmit antenna, the amateur guttering or other nearby metallic joints. It is not that common.

Fig 7.4 shows the frequencies of the more common intermodulation products where the two input frequencies are closely spaced. The calculation hold good for any spacing but frequencies further away from the area of concern are progressively less likely to be a problem in practice. Note that all non-linear devices can cause intermodulation products, but where this is deliberate, as in mixers or modulators, the intended products are more properly called mixer products or sidebands.

Unintended demodulation

Any wiring can pick up RF signals and conduct them in to an electronic device. Semiconductors in that device may rectify or demodulate the signal if it has any amplitude variation. A steady DC level, from an FM signal, is unlikely to upset bias-

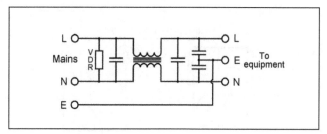

Fig 7.5. A mains filter.

ing or other DC circuits, but it is not impossible. SSB picked up by the loudspeaker leads of an audio system, for example, may be demodulated and could get into the audio amplifier stages and be amplified to be heard on the loudspeakers. Ferrite rings on the loudspeaker leads will minimise the RF getting into the amplifier and being demodulated. The rings must be at the amplifier end of the speaker leads.

Ghosting

Ghosting is not an amateur or TV defect but a propagation artefact. The signal is received direct from the transmitter and indirectly off a large metal object or reflective flat surface. Many office windows are metalised to reduce glare and can be highly reflective, especially at VHF, UHF and microwave. Two images are seen. Re orienting the TV aerial may help or moving it to the far side of the roof when some shielding might be available. Digital TV should be less susceptible but data corruption due to multipath reception is always possible.

Filters

Most of the circuits were covered in Section 3 Advanced. Specific ones to look at are the mains filter, the braid breaking filter and the ferrite ring.

Fig 7.5 shows the circuit of a mains filter. It is a low-pass filter allowing 50Hz through but blocking RF. Note that the capacitors are special mains rated types and ordinary capacitors, even rated at 1kV, must not be used on the mains. The VDR is a voltage-dependent resistor. It has a very high resistance below about 500V but a lower resistance above that. Its purpose it to absorb the energy in voltage spikes, limiting their effect on the equipment.

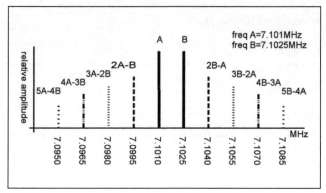

Fig 7.4. Intermodulation products from two closely spaced strong signals.

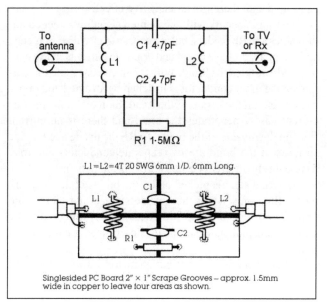

Fig 7.6. A braid breaking filter.

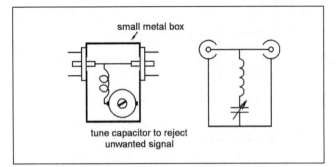

Fig 7.7. Construction of notch filter.

As an aside, it should be noted that a 0·3μF capacitor will pass about 20mA at 240V 50Hz. If the filter capacitors on any one circuit add up to more than that, then they may trip an RCD and could also result in an apparent fail of a portable appliance safety test (PAT test).

Fig 7.6 shows a braid breaking filter for use in TV down leads. Normally these are inserted in the short tail from the wall to the TV and will be fitted at the TV end.

A notch filter is simply a narrow filter, normally used to remove a fixed frequency interference. **Fig 7.7** shows such a filter, designed to be put in the aerial lead to the TV. The trimmer is adjusted for rejection of the unwanted signal.

A notch can also be formed using a λ/4 length of feeder connected in parallel with the feeder or signal path. If the free end is open circuit then at the frequency it is λ/4 the connected end will be a short circuit and will strongly attenuate an offending signal. This is called a coaxial stub.

Ferrite rings

The ferrite ring works by inserting inductance in the circuit. On single leads, such as the base of a transistor, the inductance will suppress higher frequencies and may prevent parasitic oscillations. On feeders and mains cables it suppresses unwanted RF but not the wanted signal.

There is an equal and opposite current flowing in the two conductors of power leads, AC or DC. RF pickup typically flows equally in the same direction along all the conductors, creating a magnetic field that 'sees' the inductance of the ferrite ring. The power currents cancel out so there is no magnetic field and, therefore no inductive effect.

The same occurs with the wanted signal in screened audio cables and RF feeders, but is less easy to visualise. Screened audio signals do have equal and opposite currents in the centre conductor and the braid. With RF in coaxial cable the current on the inner conductor is matched by an equal and opposite current on the *inside* of the braid. Skin effect means this current hardly penetrates the braid and there is no current flow on the *outside* of the braid. To RF the inside and outside surfaces of the braid are two separate conductors and may have entirely different currents flowing along them.

External signals picked up by the braid acting as an antenna, flow only down the outside surface and there is no opposite current to balance it. There is a resulting magnetic field and the inductance of the ferrite ring attenuates that current.

The current flowing *up* one conductor and *down* the other, even if AC, are differential mode currents. A current flowing in the same direction along both conductors is a common mode current.

Field Strength

Reducing the transmit power to the minimum required for the contact is the easiest way to minimise EMC problems. If the gain of the antenna is quoted with reference to a dipole then the field strength is given by the formula:

$$E = \frac{7\sqrt{ERP}}{d} \text{ V/m}$$

where ERP is the effective radiated power and d is the distance from the antenna in metres.

Antennas

At Foundation level, we learnt to keep antennas as far away as possible and the field strength formula shows why.

House wiring tends to act as a vertical monopole. The horizontal wiring behaves as a capacitance to ground, which has the effect of increasing the current flow in the vertical sections. Consequently, pickup tends to be greater from vertically polarised RF fields.

A horizontal dipole tends to have less interaction with house wiring, but proximity to overhead wiring such as phone lines should be considered. The feed should leave vertically, so it does not unbalance the dipole or pick up and re-radiate the RF. This applies to coaxial cables with a balun at the dipole centre or twin feed with a balun at ground level. With the latter arrangement the balun should be RF earthed and the coaxial feed buried. It should also be earthed at the point of entry to the house or shack.

Sample Questions

There are eight EMC question to be tackled in the Advanced examination.

Question	Syllabus Item
44	7a.1
45	7a.2, 7a.3
46	7a.4, 7a.5, 7a.6
47	7b.1, 7b.2
48	7b.3, 7b.4, 7b.5
49	7c.1
50	7d.1, 7e.1
51	7f.1

a7a1-1

Which amateur band has a harmonic falling within the TV intermediate frequencies?

A   40m.

B   20m.

C   12m.

D   10m.

a7a2-1

Which mode of transmission is most likely to be a cause of cross-modulation?

A   SSB.

B   FM.

C   PSK.

D   RTTY.

a7a3-1
Which transmission risks overloading a TV mast-head preamplifier
A   2m FM
B   40m SSB
C   80m CW
D   10GHz TV.

a7a4-1
A 7MHz SSB transmission is heard as a voice like signal in a neighbours music system that has a medium wave and VHF FM receiver as well as a CD player. Tests reveal it does not matter which audio input is selected, it simply needs to be switched on. A possible explanation is that
A   a harmonic of the transmission falls on the IF of the receiver
B   the signal is being picked up on the speaker leads and detected in a p-n junction
C   sufficient signal is being picked up for its envelope to excite the loudspeakers
D   there is direct pickup into the very sensitive CD laser amplifier.

a7a5-1
It is noticed that when a nearby amateur operates on 3·78MHz, his voice and another female voice on 3·60MHz are both heard interfering with a world service broadcast on 3·96MHz. Inspections of both amateur stations give them a clean bill of health. The interference may be caused by
A   one of the amateur stations overdriving their PA
B   a corroded contact in some metalwork
C   an image frequency in the receiver
D   a fault on the world service transmitter.

a7a6-1
A neighbour complains that he is getting a repeat TV picture about 1cm to the right of the real picture, especially on bold sharp edges. You should
A   check you log for any correlation with the times of the complaint
B   advise the neighbour that he needs to get a filter fitted in his aerial lead
C   say that it is not something that could be caused by amateur radio
D   suggest that the neighbour calls Ofcom to get the matter sorted out.

a7b1-1
What should the point marked 'X' in the drawing be connected to?
A   The centre of a balanced feeder.
B   The earth point on an antenna tuning unit.
C   The safety earth point on a transmitter.
D   The braid of the feeder connection on a balun.

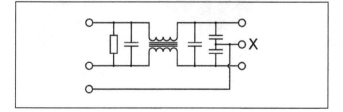

a7b2-1
Several ferrite rings are fitted over a two-wire ribbon feeder. This is found to have no effect on the transmitted signal. Why?
A   The ferrite is not very effective at radio frequencies.
B   The RF currents are in phase in each conductor and have no net effect.
C   The transmitted signal is a common mode signal and not affected by the ferrite.
D   The transmitted signal is a differential mode signal and not affected by the ferrite.

a7b3-1
Tests suggest that RF is being picked up on the loudspeaker leads of a music system and the speech is heard from the loudspeakers. Which cure is most likely to be effective?
A   Fitting ferrite rings at the loudspeaker ends of the leads.
B   Fitting ferrite rings at the amplifier ends of the loudspeaker leads.
C   Fitting 0·1μF capacitors across the loudspeaker terminals.
D   Fitting 1000μF capacitors in series with the speaker leads.

a7b4-1
The drawing shows a coaxial stub to remove a 2m amateur signal from a 100MHz VHF transmission. The stub should be
A   λ/4 long at 145MHz and open circuit at the free end
B   λ/2 long at 145MHz and open circuit at the free end
C   λ/4 long at 100MHz and open circuit at the free end
D   λ/2 long at 100MHz and open circuit at the free end.

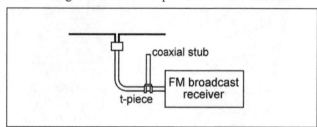

a7b5-1
A 2m amateur antenna and a broadcast TV antenna are mounted on the same roof. To minimise the risk of problems it is helpful to fit a
A   high-pass filter in the TV down lead
B   low-pass filter in the TV down lead
C   high-pass filter in the amateur feeder
D   low pass filter in the amateur feeder.

a7c1-1
The field strength 20m away from an antenna of 10dB gain fed with 40W is
A   7V/m
B   140V/m
C   0·08W/m²
D   0·8W/m².

a7d1-1

Minimum coupling between an HF dipole antenna and the feeder is achieved by

A using balanced feeder from the dipole down to ground level.

B twisting the balanced feeder to get at least one half twist per quarter wavelength

C keeping the dipole elements and the feeder, balanced or coaxial, at right angles

D using a balun and a ferrite choke on the feeder, close to the dipole.

a7e1-1

When installing an amateur transceiver in a vehicle, it is important to

A connect the radio to a circuit which is dead when the ignition key is removed

B keep the antenna and feeder well away from the vehicle wiring

C check the auxiliary position on the ignition switch is adequately rated

D mount the transceiver on the dashboard where it can be easily seen.

a7f1-1

An old telephone belonging to a neighbour is suffering from interference from HF SSB. A possible cure to try is to

A fit capacitors of about $0.01\mu F$ across the input terminals in the phone

B connect a $100\mu H$ choke in series with each lead of the telephone

C clip ferrite rings over the lead to the phone or wind round a ring if possible

D replace the phone with a modern electronic version.

8. Operating Practices and Procedures

When 'on-air' you are a voice of amateur radio, an ambassador for the hobby and it is essential to give a good impression. Courtesy and consideration for other, other views and their cultures is key. Bad language must be avoided and if you overhear such language or receive discourteous remarks it is very important not to respond to it. Pretend you have not heard it, if necessary simply find another frequency. Music is not appropriate for the same reason. Don't get drawn into conversation; often that is the intent of whoever is transmitting such material.

Calling CQ

When calling CQ or selecting a working frequency it is necessary to listen and ask if the frequency is in use because someone in range may be listening to someone who is further away. On VHF and UHF FM there is a set calling channel so asking if that is in use is not necessary and a short CQ call, repeated once will be sufficient to get a response if anybody is awaiting a call. You then need to move (QSY) to a working channel, leaving the calling channel free.

On HF SSB two things are different. There is no set calling channel and *netting* on frequency is required. Calls must be repeated frequently so that a person tuning round will find you rather than tune past. The call must also be longer to enable effective netting, that is tuning carefully on frequency to avoid the audio sounding way off pitch.

Phonetic alphabet

The phonetic alphabet is the same throughout the world and should be used when communication is difficult. The licence permits any common word but other words may only be common to English speakers. 'Spain' begins with an 'E' in many other languages, including Spanish. It is not difficult to learn and you may be asked in the exam. See the reference section for the phonetic alphabet.

Log

The licence no longer demands log keeping, but it remains advised best practice. EMC questions do assume a log is kept although there are no exam questions specifically on log keeping itself. A log will be needed especially to collect QSL cards for contests and awards.

Repeaters and band plans

The band plan shows how amateurs have decided how best to allocate sections of the bands to different uses. This allows many more amateurs to use the bands without intolerable interference to each other. Band plans are not mandatory, like obeying your licence is, but operating outside the band plan is particularly unpopular and you risk both causing and suffering from interference. The examination may include a question on the 20m (14MHz) band and the 2m (145MHz) bands. A simplified band plan is provided for use. The 145MHz plan shows the portion used by repeaters.

A repeater has its own separate licence and can transmit and receive simultaneously. Different frequencies are required and repeaters in the 2m band listen on an input frequency, which is 600kHz lower than the output frequency. A repeater 'on' 145. 700MHz will transmit on that frequency, where you must listen, but receives on 145. 100MHz where you must transmit.

To prevent unintended RF noises being re-transmitted the repeater uses a technique known as CTCSS, continuous tone controlled squelch system. The CTCSS tone is a sub-audible tone, below 300Hz and each region of the UK is allocated its own tone. Signals in to the repeater will be ignored unless the correct tone is present. This also avoids problems where an amateur is on a prominent site and their RF is reaching two repeaters on that RF channel. Only the one using the appropriate tone will respond.

To use a repeater the CTCSS facility needs to be turned on, having been told the correct tone to use, and the repeater frequency offset must be enabled so the transmitter drops 600kHz when the PTT (press to talk switch or button) is pressed.

Older repeaters used a 1750Hz audible tone as an access tone, this is being phased out but some do still exist.

Desk microphones and TNCs

Most VHF and UHF transceivers come supplied with a fist microphone and the output level will be correct for that transceiver. Desk microphones and TNCs (a type of modem) will have a different level and will need adjusting or a small interface provided to ensure correct levels and correct operation of the PTT.

A TNC is a terminal node controller, a PC modem for packet radio that also recognises when messages are addressed to it by callsign and may have message storage capability. This function can also be performed in software and use the PC sound card. The comment on getting the levels and PTT operation correct are equally applicable. Many other data modes are possible with a PC, but are not discussed at Foundation level.

Practical Assessment

The remainder of this section of the syllabus is assessed as a practical demonstration. This can be done as part of a training course (strongly advised), in isolation, or as part of the overall examination. Most advertised exams are only that and do not automatically include the practical assessment. If you are self-taught and not on a course, do check what you are signing up for when it comes to the exam.

Sample Questions

There are two questions in this area, taken from syllabus items 8a.1, 8a.2, 8a.3, 8a.4, 8b.1, 8c.1, 8d.1. The only constraint is that the questions will come from different syllabus items.

f8a1-1

One should ask if the frequency is in use because

A   it lets others listening on the frequency know it is about to be used

B   you could interfere with someone listening to a more distant station

C   that is the procedure laid down in the amateur licence

D   it might not be your turn to use that frequency.

f8a2-1

The purpose of a much longer CQ call on HF SSB is to

A   overcome the limitations of HF propagation to ensure your call is heard

B   allow people tuning round to tune correctly on to your transmission

C   encourage people listening to reply to you rather than someone else

D   transmit for long enough that other stations realise the frequency is in use.

f8a3-1

When replying to a CQ call on 2m FM you can expect the person calling CQ to

A   ask you your name and start a conversation

B   give the location and details of their station

C   ask you to wait while they find a clear channel

D   call CQ again to see if anybody else wants to join in.

f8a4-1

The correct phonetic spelling of the word NOVEMBER is

A   november oscar victor echo may bravo echo romeo

B   nut oscar victor echo mike bravo echo romeo

C   nut oscar victor easy mike bravo easy romeo

D   november oscar victor echo mike bravo echo romeo

f8a5-1

Which action is not considered appropriate when in contact by amateur radio?

A   Playing a short favourite piece of music.

B   Discussing the results of a football match seen on TV.

C   Giving your name using the phonetic alphabet.

D   Discussing a club meeting with another amateur.

f8a6-1

When calling CQ you receive a reply giving a valid callsign but using rude language. You should

A   reply to the contact but remain polite

B   reply saying you do not like that kind of language

C   tell the person that you will report them to the RSGB

D   ignore the reply as if you had not heard it

f8b1-1

To reduce the risk of an amateur on a hilltop transmitting into two repeaters at the same time, the repeaters

A   are all on different radio frequencies

B   on the same radio frequency are too far apart

C   on the same radio frequency have different sub-audio tones

D   are connected together so only the stronger one responds.

f8c1-1

Having just enjoyed a Morse practice session, you decide to listen on-air for a Morse transmission. A likely frequency to listen to is

A   14· 055MHz

B   14· 120MHz

C   144· 725MHz

D   144· 900MHz.

f8d1-1

When connecting a computer sound card to the microphone socket of your radio you should

A   check that the SWR has not been affected

B   send CQ PC as a call instead of the normal CQ call

C   save the frequency and mode in the radio's memory

D   check the audio level is correct and the PTT operation.

INTERMEDIATE

Q-codes, RST codes, abbreviations and callsign prefixes

You are expected to known the Q codes QRL, QRM, QRN, QRP, QRT, QRZ, QSB, QSL, QSO, QSY and QTH. The abbreviations CQ, DE, DX, R, RST, SIG, UR and WX are also examined. These are all shown in the reference section.

RST stands for Readability, Signal Strength and Tone. Readability is on a 5-point scale with R5 a very good easily readable signal and R1 barely readable at all, ie mostly unreadable. The signal strength is on a 9-point scale with S9 a very strong signal and S1 a barely perceptible one. The tone is only relevant to Morse and stems from the different ways of generating a tone historically. Some of the imperfections are now very unlikely to occur and most signals will be T9, which is very good.

Each county has its own callsign prefix allocated by the ITU, International Telecommunications Union. They are required for all radio signals, not just amateurs, but the format of amateur callsigns is defined so it is recognisable as amateur. The UK has G, M and 2 and small sections of other letter sequences that are used for maritime licences. The prefixes EI, F, I, JA, PA, VE. VK and ZL are examined and are shown in the reference section.

Other prefixes and the details of amateurs that have released their details are available in 'call books' such as the *RSGB Yearbook*. That is a compendium of useful information and a listing of callsigns, names and addresses similar to a telephone directory. It is necessary, when taking out an amateur licence, to signify if your own details are to be available for publication or not.

Modes

The different modes have different merits as regards distance obtainable at a set power. This is different from the order of merit in EMC terms and care should be taken to check the context of the question, EMC or operational.

Morse code (CW) is still very effective at getting a message through with limited power or poor propagation conditions. The more sophisticated data methods can now achieve better results, but those developments are relatively recent and are not examined.

SSB is the most effective of the voice modes since all the power is concentrated in one sideband and narrow filtering and deliberately offsetting the filter or varying the slope can cut out a particular interferer without doing too much damage to the wanted signal. Again, digital techniques can make further improvements but that is much more recent and also not examined.

FM is the least effective at achieving the greatest range but is inherently resistant to many common types of interference, which affect the amplitude and are ignored by an FM discriminator. The audio quality is normally superior to SSB and does not suffer from frequency offsets influencing the audio pitch.

The licence does not specify modes of transmission and many other modes and techniques have been developed, aided greatly by the use of PCs and sound cards. Among the earliest systems was RTTY, radio teletype, which used an external modem to translate the DC levels into audio tones or used the DC to directly set the change in RF carrier frequency. Today that is also done using a PC sound card.

Packet radio is a data mode, normally 1200 bits/second data rate with 8 bits to define a character. Usually a separate modem, a TNC (Terminal Node Controller), is used. This is similar to the modem used to connect a PC to a phone line, but it also contains the means of identifying which signals are addressed to that station, and storing them to be read later. Each packet of data must be acknowledged and that permits packets erroneously received to be re-sent. Those tasks can be done by a PC, but does require the PC to be left running.

PSK31 is another data mode using a clever method of modulation that minimises the bandwidth needed, allowing a narrow clear slot to be utilised in an otherwise crowded band. Newer methods that are even more sophisticated are being developed all the time, particularly in the area of narrow bandwidth or recovery of signals buried in the noise and interference of other users.

SSTV and FSTV are slow scan TV and 'normal' fast scan TV. FSTV requires very high bandwidths, which are only available in the frequency bands above 1·2GHz. Slow scan uses voice bandwidths and can be sent world-wide on HF. It takes a few seconds to send a single picture, longer if in colour, as most are. FSTV uses a normal TV camera but SSTV typically uses a webcam and PC.

Having made a contact, some amateurs send *QSL cards*, like a postcard, to confirm the contact. These are used as evidence of the contact for awards such as for 100 countries or different islands. More locally, grid squares can be used; some amateurs may use a boat to activate a 'wet' square or a tiny island.

Contests usually involve contacting as many stations as possible, particularly at great distances or in different countries or continents, and the scoring rules may permit the number of contacts to be multiplied by the number of different countries to provide the final score. The log is used as evidence and everybody's log is cross-checked for consistency. The information exchanged usually consists of a callsign, serial number and a reference to location. Errors in logging exchanged information are penalised.

Satellites

Amateurs have launched several satellites, over 60 to date, by piggy-backing on commercial launches. We pay a fraction of the true cost but often it is still a hefty sum. Mostly these are in low earth orbit (LEO) at heights above 150km. Many are higher to reduce atmospheric drag and have a period, time per orbit, of around an hour and a half. These move rapidly in relation to a ground station and may only be visible for a few minutes per orbit and not visible at all for several orbits. Communication is only possible if both stations have visibility and the movement causes frequency changes due to the Doppler effect. The frequency offset is greatest when the relative motion is greatest, low on the horizon, and briefly zero when at closest approach, when the relative motion is zero. Computer tracking programs are readily available, providing the Doppler offsets and signals to drive azimuth and elevation antenna rotators.

The bands used by each satellite are available on the web and from the amateur user groups, AMSAT-UK in this country. The up- and down-link are usually in different bands, but remember that you must then have receive capability on both bands. The down-link band to hear the satellite and the up-link band to comply with the licence requirement to be able to receive on the frequency used for transmitting - in case you cause interference.

Satellite power is derived from solar panels and is very limited. A strong up-link signal can affect the share of the down-link power so the minimum for successful communication must be used. A common guide is to limit the up-link power such that the down-link is no stronger than the satellite beacon. However, you should check via the user group that it is the correct method for that particular satellite.

Some satellites are in higher orbits. That allows visibility from larger areas of the earth's surface and longer periods of visibility, but the greater distances may result in weaker down-link signals and potentially more users from the wider coverage.

Sample Questions

The Intermediate paper has four questions on operating, distributed round the syllabus sections as shown in the table:

Question	Syllabus Item
36	8a.1 8b.1 8c.1
37	8 d.1 8e.1 8e.2
38	8f.1 8f.2 8f.3 8f.4
39	8g.1 8g.2 8g.3 8g.4

i8a1-1

The Q code indication you are suffering from fading is

A   QSB

B   QFA

C   QRL

D   QST.

i8b1-1

The abbreviation DE means

A   addressed to

B   from

C   route via

D   received OK.

i8c1-1
The signal report 2 and 5 means
A   a weak signal and very difficult to read
B   a weak signal but still very clear to read
C   a fairly strong signal but is hard to understand
D   a fairly strong signal and a clear one.

i8d1-1
A battery operated transmitter is likely to have the greatest range if used to send
A   CW
B   FM
C   SSB
D   AM

i8e1-1
The modes of operation available at the Intermediate licence level are
A   AM, FM, SSB and CW only
B   voice modes and CW only
C   voice, TV and CW only
D   not limited in any way.

i8e2-1
Sending several different types of data signal
A   requires a large assortment of suitable modems
B   normally required modification to the modulator in the transmitter
C   can be readily achieved using a PC with a sound card
D   may require an extension such as a Notice of Variation to the licence.

i8f1-1
The address to send a QSL card to a UK amateur can be found from
A   the Radio Society of Great Britain
B   a call book or yearbook
C   a telephone directory
D   the local authority voters list.

i8f2-1
One purpose of sending QSL cards is to
A   remember the names and details of the contacts you have made
B   confirm a contact for the purpose of an operating award
C   collect sufficient points to upgrade the class of licence
D   demonstrate you are still actively engaged in amateur radio.

i8f3-1
PA3DX replies to a CQ call. For a better signal you should turn the beam towards
A   the Netherlands
B   Sweden
C   Belgium
D   Iceland.

i8f4-1
When taking part in a competition such as the VHF Field Day, you would normally give
A   your callsign and first name
B   the date of renewal of your licence
C   your call sign and the serial number of the contact
D   a secret password issued by the competition organisers.

i8g1-1
You propose to demonstrate amateur radio and operation through a satellite at a local exhibition. The organiser allocates the time slot 11.30 till 12 am for this. This time
A   should get plenty of satellite contacts because it is a weekend
B   may or may not correspond with the time a satellite is in view
C   should be pre-booked with the local satellite user group
D   advertised well in advance to ensure a good audience.

i8g2-1
Operation through a satellite will require
A   the correct CTCSS tone to access the satellite
B   two receivers to cover both uplink and downlink bands
C   a single transceiver which can change from Tx to Rx quickly
D   a substantial power amplifier due to the greater range required.

i8g3-1
While watching a demonstration of satellite operation you notice the received frequency is being frequently adjusted. This is because
A   the satellite transmit frequency depends on the changing power to its solar panels
B   it is not possible to correct any frequency instability in the satellite transmitter
C   satellite signals are being diffracted though the ionosphere
D   of the Doppler effect caused by the satellite motion.

i8g4-1
Transmitting a strong signal to an amateur satellite is
A   required to overcome the greater distances to the satellite
B   likely to result in an unfair share of the downlink transmit power
C   not necessary but unlikely to have any undesirable effect
D   only required after closest approach and the range is increasing.

ADVANCED

Packet Radio
Packet is a data system of interconnected users and nodes. There are two basic methods of use. Bulletin boards act as common mailboxes allowing a user to log on to collect and send their mail. The message is addressed to the other user at their mailbox, g4abc@gb7hsn for example. For boxes outside the UK country addressing is required. As the name implies data is divided up into packets with address headers and routed through the system. Each packet is error checked at each stage. It may go entirely by radio, possibly by HF radio to another country, possibly by amateur satellite but more commonly now via an internet connection that is unseen by the end users. The entire message is reconstituted at each node and then sent on to the destination mailbox to await the recipient logging on to collect their mail. This is known as store-and-forward protocol.

Amateurs can connect directly to each other if in range, similar to VHF FM voice coverage, or can route via nodes by setting up the route themselves. Each packet is sent individually but is error checked each 'hop'.

Finally it is possible to route via another amateur who is better located by digipeating. That amateurs station simply retransmits each burst of data as soon as it is received, provided the channel is clear. Error checking is only performed on an end-to-end basis. The odds of errors increase for each digipeated hop so throughput tends to be lower but if you are located in a poor signal area digipeating is a good way out.

Repeaters

Accessing repeaters was covered at Foundation level, except the offset on 70cm is +1· 6MHz. That is, the repeater listens above its output on 70cm. There are wide split repeaters with a +7· 6MHz offset and, more recently, digital voice repeaters with a different offset. The audio signal is sampled, digitised and sent as a data stream.

Some repeaters have a time-out to stop excessively long 'overs'. This means a short pause is needed when another station accesses the repeater to reset the timer. Often that is signified by a short beep as the repeater releases its PTT.

Contests and Special Events

Contesting can be both fun and educational but care needs to be taken setting up the station since often equipment is used together in untried configurations seeking maximum sensitivity and maximum transmit power. This can easily lead to overdriving the PA so it bcomes non-linear and splatters over adjacent frequencies.

Similarly, the use of a pre-amplifier can overload the receiver front end especially when high powers are being used by most stations. The received signal seems to splatter over adjacent frequencies. This can lead to disputes as to the real cause.

Reducing the transmit power will solve the problem but will not identify the cause. To do that, beam away at the receive site. If the receiver was overloaded the splatter should drop faster than the signal and may cease entirely. If the receiver was still in its linear range and the fault is at the transmitter, the relative levels of signal and splatter will be unchanged; both will be equally weaker.

Contest stations may use a personal callsign, a club callsign or a special contest callsign available to the top contesters for a few set contests. They are in the format G2X, ie a single letter after the number and the G or M.

Special events are to commemorate a worthy occasion and provide an opportunity to demonstrate amateur radio to the public. Special callsigns can be obtained, normally beginning GB, a number and two of three letters. Sometimes an anniversary can be celebrated as GB100X, but that takes special arrangements. Special event stations must be open to the public.

Band Plans

The IARU (International Amateur Radio Union) produces band plans, which are a 'gentleman's agreement' on usage inside the bands prescribed by the licence. Some items to add at this level are:

- No SSB operation in the 10MHz (30m) band;
- No contests in the 10MHz (30m), 18MHz (17m) and 24MHz (12m) bands;
- Narrow band modes are at the lower end of each band;
- Normally lower sideband below 10MHz, upper sideband above.

As before, questions will be on the 14MHz and 144MHz bands and this time the real IARU plan will be used, not a simplified version.

Sample Questions

There are four questions on operating.

Question	Syllabus Item
52	8a.1
53	8b.1
54	8c.1, 8d.1
55	8e.1

a8a1-1

Messages are stored complete and automatically forwarded in a
A   Repeater
B   Digipeater
C   Node
D   BBS.

a8a1-2

Messages are stored complete and delivered when requested in a
A   BBS
B   Node
C   Digipeater
D   Repeater.

a8b1-1

It is noticed that when a small group of amateurs are using a repeater, that occasionally an over, even a short one, is blocked by a series of beeps. This is because
A   one of the amateurs is transmitting off-frequency
B   some of the messages are of a grossly offensive character
C   the annual subscription to the repeater group is outstanding
D   some users are not waiting for the reset tone before transmitting.

a8c1-1

There is a dispute during a contest as to whether the distant transmitter is being overdriven or the local receiver is being driven into non-linearity. A suitable test for this would be to
A   reduce the drive to the transmitter and see if the splatter ceases
B   insert an attenuator in the feeder to the receiver and note the effect
C   tune the receiver to a different transmission to see if that has the same problem
D   QSY both stations 10kHz or more to a clear frequency and try again.

a8d1-1

While tuning round the call "CQ CQ de GB3NOV" is heard. The callsign indicates that the station
A   belongs to an amateur in Great Britain
B   is celebrating an special event or occasion
C   belongs to a club putting non-licensed persons on the air
D   is transmitting under a special research Notice of Variation.

a8e1-1

To allow more foreign stations to enter a contest it is decided to increase the number of bands used. Four suggestions are on the table, which one should be chosen?
A   80m, 40m, 30m and 20m.
B   40m, 20m, 17m and 15m.
C   40m, 20m, 15m and 10m.
D   20m, 15m, 12m and 10m.

9. Safety

Clearly safety is the most important issue in any activity, but what are the risks associated with amateur radio?

High voltages and currents

The dangers of high voltages are perhaps the most obvious. The voltages do not need to be all that high if the shock is across the chest and the skin is moist, allowing good contact. 36 volts has been recorded as causing a fatality by current across the chest disrupting the heart rhythm.

Even small batteries can source high currents, sufficient to cause a ring or metal band to get red hot, a wire explode in a shower of molten metal, or cause a fire.

Domestic equipment may be double insulated and marked with the double square symbol shown in **Fig 9.1**. Those items do not have any exposed or accessible metalwork and do not need an earth connection. All other devices *must* be fitted with an earth lead, the mains safety earth, unless of course it is battery powered. Mains powered amateur radio equipment does have exposed metalwork, even if it is only the body of the RF socket on the back. It *must* have a safety earth and should have an RF earth if it is a transmitter. See the EMC section again!

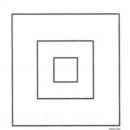

Fig 9.1. The double insulated symbol. Equipment with this mark does not require an earth connection. If not marked as double insulated an earth *must* be fitted.

At Foundation level the advice is simple, do not work inside live equipment, disconnect it and pull the plug out. Live work should be left to those who are qualified.

PME

PME is a particular wiring method of supplying power to your house, especially newer houses. The details are outside the scope of the syllabus but you should know that you must get further advice if this is the case. Further details are available on the RSGB EMC Committee web site. You may need to get professional advice appropriate to your circumstances and check your supply type from your electricity supplier.

Fuses

All equipment must be fused. The correct fuse to use should be marked on the equipment or in its handbook or operating instructions. Do not fit a larger fuse.

There are two risks. Wires inside mains equipments may become detached or loose and touch the (metal) case, making it live. The case is earthed so the fuse will blow, cutting the power. An internal fault may cause excessive current to flow,

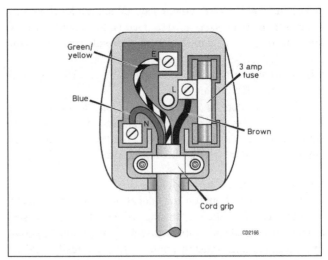

Fig 9.2. A correctly wired mains plug. All three wires must be secure, no exposed conductors and no stray strands. Cord grip traps outer sheath.

resulting in overheating and a fire. If severe the fuse may blow, but it is possible a fire could be started at currents below that needed to blow the fuse.

If you smell burning, see smoke or fire, don't touch it, switch off at the wall plug or the main off switch (see below). If you don't know what to do next, get out and get help, now!

Wiring a plug

You are not expected to wire a mains plug, that is for the Intermediate practical assessment, but you do need to be able to recognise a correctly wired plug. **Fig 9.2** shows a correctly wired plug.

Switch off

There should be a single master OFF switch and everybody in the house should know where it is. In any incident or accident involving electricity, the first action is always to switch off the power. If you touch a casualty while they are still connected to the mains, you will become a casualty yourself. Switch off and get help if you are unsure.

Tidy shack

A well laid out tidy shack is safer to work in as well as having good EMC characteristics. Trailing wires are trip hazards or risk pulling equipment on the floor, risking damage, exposed live wires and maybe fire. Running wires under carpets may look better but they will get frayed and the first you notice is a burning smell or a blown fuse. Run cables in proper trays, conduits or clips. Elevated wires and feeders must be securely fixed and out of harms way - to you or the cable.

Feeders and antennas

The same applies to antennas. At 10W of RF an RF burn is not likely, but will you reroute when you upgrade? Exposed antennas should be out of reach, as high RF voltages can occur at points along an antenna even at modest power levels.

Running antennas and feeders close to power cables is a potential EMC hazard. If they come in contact, especially with overhead power cables, it could become a serious safety hazard as well. From inside you might not notice.

Erecting feeders and antennas can be hazardous, there should always be someone in a relatively safe position and an adult must be present.

Particularly high antennas may need lightning protection. This is a specialised subject and the local authority planning and building department may be able to assist or point you in the right direction. They will also advise if you need planning permission.

Headphones

Using headphones can damage your hearing. It is very easy to turn up the volume trying to copy a weak station and then listen at high volume for long periods. It may take years for this to cause damage, but by the time you realise it will also be years too late. The trick is to keep turning the volume down until it is too quiet, then come up a bit. Many people tend to turn up until it almost seems too loud. That is the wrong way to do it: keep it down.

The headphones may create a metallic contact making any electric shock worse. Not an issue if you don't service live equipment, but something to remember for later.

Sample Questions

Two questions on safety.

Question	Syllabus Item
24	9a.1, 9a.2, 9a.3, 9a.4, 9a.5, 9c.1, 9c.2, 9c.3, 9c.4, 9c.5, 9c.6, 9d.1
25	9a.6, 9b.1

f9a1-1
The danger associated with a low voltage but a high current is
A electrocution
B very hot metal
C blown fuses
D high SWR.

f9a2-1
A label next to the fuse box in your house says the supply is of a type known as PME. What, if anything, should you do?
A No need to do anything, it is not applicable to amateur radio.
B Check further about getting proper advice for your particular circumstances.
C Disconnect the mains earth lead to the shack.
D Ask the electricity supply company to arrange a different supply.

f9a3-1
The MOST SERIOUS effect of fitting a fuse of the wrong rating is that the
A equipment might be damaged
B fuse might not blow when it should
C fuse might blow when it shouldn't
D fuse will be damaged.

f9a4-1
When working inside a mains power supply for a transmitter
A you should ensure you are properly earthed
B the device must be switched off and unplugged
C power must be applied to check the work is correct
D the equipment should be placed on a rubber mat.

f9a5-1
In a mains plug the correct connection for the wires is
A Live – brown Neutral – blue Earth – green/yellow
B Live – blue Neutral – brown Earth – green/yellow
C Live – brown Neutral – green/yellow Earth – blue
D Live – blue Neutral – green/yellow Earth – brown.

f9a6-1
The reason for having a single switch to turn off everything in the radio shack is
A that there are usually lots of items with separate switches and it is easy to miss one
B that it is quick and safe to be sure to cut all power in the event of an accident
C to save time switching lots of different items on one at a time
D it could be damaging to power amplifiers to switch things on in the wrong order.

f9b1-1
On finding someone laying on the floor in a tangle of wires, the FIRST action is to
A check for breathing and a pulse
B switch off all the power
C phone for an ambulance
D remove any wires round the neck.

f9c1-1
One risk of having wires routed under the carpet is that
A you might trip over it
B it could be overlooked when disconnecting something
C it is more likely to radiate
D it may get frayed and not be noticed.

f9c2-1
Elevated wires and feeders
A are more likely to radiate
B reduce the possibility of electric shock
C should be suitably positioned and fixed
D must be run in earthed metal conduit.

f9c3-1

The main problem with the antenna arrangement in the diagram is that

A   noise on the power line can be induced in the antenna making receiving harder

B   the antenna leads over the shack risking RF pickup in the shack

C   there is a risk that RF could be induced into the power line

D   the antenna can fall on to the power line.

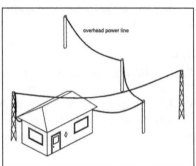

overhead power line

f9c4-1

An adult should be present when

A   erecting an antenna at height

B   assembling a Yagi antenna

C   planning the layout of the shack

D   supervising another M3 licensee operating your equipment.

f9c5-1

A transmitting antenna should be

A   adjusted for maximum SWR

B   aligned in North-South position

C   fed from the end nearest the house

D   mounted where it cannot be touched.

f9c6-1

Lightning protection should be considered if the antenna is

A   supported on metal poles

B   unbalanced or end-fed

C   particularly high

D   vertical.

f9d1-1

A key danger, while using headphones, often not noticed until it is too late is

A   using headphones with a metallic headband

B   listening to CW for lengthy periods

C   setting the squelch at too high a level

D   having the volume a bit too loud.

INTERMEDIATE

The practical assessment for the Intermediate licence is centred on constructional projects, soldering and the use of tools. These bring a new crop of safety considerations to avoid injury.

Soldering

The soldering iron gets hot enough to burn and may, if left on flammable material, either start a fire or trigger fire alarms. A proper stand must be used. The flux in the solder produces fumes which can be an irritant, particularly to asthmatics and can splash and boil risking hot flux or molten solder in the eyes. The soldering area must be well ventilated and eye protection worn.

Using tools

The biggest risk is careless use and using the wrong tool. The work should be held securely in a vice or other appropriate method of restraint. Power drills rotate at high speed and will eject a chuck key with considerable force. Check twice, first that it has not been left in the drill and then that it is somewhere out of the way. A centre punch will help guide the drill into the correct place and reduce the risk of it wandering. If available a pillar mounted drill is more secure, unable to wander and usually produces a much neater job. The guard must be used and eye protection should be worn to prevent swarf, the little bits produced when drilling, flying off into the eyes.

Working at height.

The risk is dropped tools and falls. The correct angle for a ladder is 4:1. A ladder reaching 4m up the wall should be 1m out from the wall at the base. It must be fixed at the top or properly held at the bottom. Position the ladder so reaching out to the side is avoided.

A tool belt will ensure you have the right tools with you, but, more importantly, help avoid dropped tools. Nonetheless, all involved should be wearing hard hats. If there are overhead power lines, common in rural communities, then contact with the ladder or a person on it is potentially fatal. Keep well clear of power lines to avoid contact or arcing across. Consider the possibility of falling on to them if the ladder slips sideways.

Fuses

Normally an appliance will be marked with the correct fuse or stated in its operating instructions. Failing that the value can be worked out using the formula:

$$\text{Current} = \frac{\text{power}}{230} \text{ A}$$

Not all values of fuse are available. The smallest one larger than the calculation should be used. Do *not* use a 13A fuse because you happen to have one, go and get the correct fuse and don't use it until then. Keep a small stock.

RCD

An RCD is a residual current device. Do not confuse this with a circuit breaker.

A circuit breaker is an automatic fuse. It is often quicker than a fuse and gives better protection in that it triggers even on slight excess currents when a fuse might take quite some time to blow.

An RCD detects when something is in contact with the live wires and cuts the power. It normally triggers at 30mA and does so quickly. If something touches the live wire, some current flows through that and not back the neutral. The RCD notices the difference in current and triggers to that. An RCD is not a fuse or circuit breaker and does not detect excess current, only when the live and neutral currents are different.

A fuse or circuit breaker must always be fitted to guard against excess current and consequent overheating and fire. An RCD provides better protection against electric shock. Use both!

Other electrical hazards

High voltages and high currents were covered at the Foundation level. They are not examined specifically but a re-read is always advisable.

Large capacitors can remain charged when disconnected or the device is switched off. Good designs include a high value resistor across such capacitors so they discharge soon after the power is removed. Don't assume there is one, discharge using a resistor yourself and don't touch while you are doing it!

RF

At Intermediate level we are using powers that can be harmful. A microwave oven uses RF to heat the food and the RF from amateur transmitters can cause body tissue heating as well. The risk is frequency dependent and the safe levels are given in the guide produced by the Health Protection Agency (HPA) and ICNIRP, the International Committee on Non-Ionising Radiation Protection.

Higher frequencies, microwaves, called that because the wavelength is short, are more readily absorbed and the power limits are lower. The eyes are most susceptible to damage because they do not have any blood flow to remove extra heat. For that reason standing in front of high gain antennas, RF dishes and looking down waveguides is particularly silly. Don't.

Sample Questions

To ensure this matter is taken seriously, there are four question asked in the exam.

Question	Syllabus Item
40	9a.1
41	9b.1 9b.2 9b.3 9b.4 9b.5 9b.6
42	9c.1 9c.2 9c.3 9c.4
43	9d.1 9d.2 9d.3 9d.4 9e.1 9e.2 9e.3

i9a1-1

When soldering it is advisable to
A   place the work on an insulated mat
B   wear glasses or goggles
C   wear insulated rubber gloves
D   keep the window closed to retain the heat.

i9b1-1

Cuts and grazes when using tools are most likely if they
A   are kept sharp
B   get wet and rusty
C   are used carelessly
D   are kept in a tool belt.

i9b2-1

The item being worked on should be held in a vice when
A   using a drill or file
B   it is being soldered
C   there is a risk of swarf
D   wearing protective gloves.

i9b3-1

Being hit hard by a chuck key suggests
A   it has been left on the workbench
B   it was left in the chuck of the drill
C   the drill is loose and liable to wander
D   a centre-punch was not properly used.

i9b4-1

The purpose of a centre-punch is to
A   mark out the work to help drill or file in the right place
B   identify all the places where a hole needs to be drilled
C   make an indentation so the drill is less likely to wander
D   produce a pilot hole that can be seen from the other side.

i9b5-1

A risk when drilling is that
A   small particles may fly up from the drill bit
B   goggles will prevent a clear view of the work
C   the work may rotate when held in the vice
D   the hole size cannot be checked until afterwards.

ib6-1

When using a pillar mounted drill
A   goggles need not be worn
B   there is a higher risk of vibration
C   the drill is secure and unlikely to wander
D   it is not possible to leave the key in the chuck.

i9c1-1

A ladder reaches 6m up a wall. How far from the wall should the foot of the ladder be?
A   1m.
B   1·5m.
C   2m.
D   2·5m.

i9c2-1

What is wrong in the drawing?
A   The ladder is at the wrong angle.
B   Nobody is supporting the ladder at the bottom.
C   The ladder should extend above the top of the wall.
D   The person on the ladder is not wearing a hard hat.

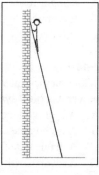

i9c3-1

You are likely to fall off a ladder if
A   you are not wearing safety shoes or boots
B   the ladder is not securely tied at the top
C   people are not wearing their hard hats
D   you reach too far out to the side.

i9c4-1

Something is missing in the drawing.
What is it?
A   The tie at the top of the ladder.
B   The antenna or feeder.
C   A safety rope.
D   A hard hat.

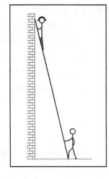

i9d1-1

The main hazard using ladders when the houses have an overhead mains supply is
A   the cables may snag on the ladder making movement more difficult
B   the risk of electric shock from coming into contact with the cables
C   routing the feeder away from the mains to avoid EMC problems
D   remembering to switch off the mains supply in the house.

i9d2-1

A suitable fuse to fit in the **mains plug** of a 20A 12V power supply is
A   1A
B   5A
C   13A
D   25A.

i9d3-1

Which statement about the mains supply to the shack is correct?
A   An RCD is better than a fuse for shock protection, but a fuse is still required.
B   If an RCD (residual current device) is used a separate fuse is not required.
C   The best protection against electric shock is achieved by using a fuse.
D   It is unwise to fit a fuse and an RCD in the same electricity supply.

i9d4-1

Which device may still give a nasty electric shock after the power has been switched off?
A   A high voltage inductor.
B   A high value capacitor.
C   A mains transformer.
D   A low pass filter.

i9e1-1

The main health effect from electromagnetic radiation is
A   loss of memory
B   tingling in the fingers
C   heating of body tissue
D   involuntary twitching.

i9e2-1

The HPA produces guidance on
A   amateur band plans
B   transmitting overseas
C   RF radiation safety limits
D   safe use of hand and power tools.

i9e3-1

Why is it unwise to look down waveguides?
A   The eyes are particularly susceptible to RF heating
B   Cooling air may blow small particles into the eyes
C   Most waveguides have sharp edges for accurate fitting
D   Waveguides contain moving parts that may poke out.

ADVANCED

At Advanced level the emphasis is on why various safety rules exist and to recognise hazardous situations. Hitherto, the advice has been to use commercially supplied items for mains use. At this level it is recognised that occasionally mains related activities are unavoidable, as is servicing live equipment so the effect of adjustments can be observed. Nonetheless, the advice remains to keep the power off whenever possible.

It is safer to make a connection with the power off and switch on to observe the results. Live adjustments must be made with insulated tools and one hand kept behind your back or in pocket so any shock does not cause current to flow across the chest. Similarly, meter prods should be in good order and well insulated. The equipment and the meter should be stable and not held in the other hand - breaking the 'one hand only' rule. Dry flooring with plastic or carpet floor covering avoids one conduction path. On concrete, a rubber mat will help.

Valve transmitting equipment employs voltage well above mains potential, 1 - 2kV is typical for PAs providing over 200W.

Portable operation outside

A particular hazard outside is your contact with earth. When setting up, it is doubly important to do as much as possible with the power off. The only safe advice is to avoid servicing live in the field. Find a suitable indoor location.

An RCD is essential. Consider having an RCD at both ends of a long supply cable. The cable must be protected from damage and ideally out of reach, although an elevated cable may pick up RF. The RCD acts if despite the precautions, there is cable damage. Then have an RCD by the main 'off' switch.

Don't overload this supply, it's not a house ring main so if plugged in a conventional socket, the limit is 13A, or less if the cable is not suitably rated. A circuit breaker is preferable to a fuse, it's quicker acting and can be reset if someone does plug an electric kettle in and trips the lot.

Mobile

Nothing must distract your safe control and attention to driving the vehicle. Adjusting controls that require you to look down should only be done whilst stationary. Amateur radio is exempt from the absolute offence of using a mobile phone while driving, but the indirect offences of driving without due care and attention / due consideration for others etc still very much apply and are highly likely to be used. Hands free is essential.

All equipment must be securely mounted so it does not become a missile in an accident, and positioned so you, or the passengers, do not fly into it. Power should be obtained by connecting a properly fused lead to battery positive or in accordance specific instructions of the vehicle manufacturer. The negative lead should be connected, unfused, to the vehicle chassis. This is a change to previous advice and is based on a revision to the industry Code of Practice FCS1362.

All wires should be properly protected from chafing and kept away from vehicle wires and the vehicle electronics to prevent RF getting into the engine control system, automatic braking and other safety related systems. The handbook or the manufacturer should be consulted for the permissible level of transmitted RF. It is quite possible that the recommended level will be well below the limit of the licence.

The transmitter now needs to be E marked as well as CE marked. E marking indicates suitability for vehicle installation provided all the installation requirements are observed. A nonstandard installation can compromise the insurance and you may then be driving uninsured.

Lightning

Tall masts may need lightning protection. A good earth at the base of the mast will divert most of the energy of a direct strike; nonetheless some damage may be expected. This can be minimised by disconnecting equipment and moving it away. A few inches separation may well be useless as such distances can easily be jumped and very high fields can induce damaging voltages in nearby conductors.

The more common risk is static charge built up due to nearby thunderstorms. This may give a severe jolt causing a secondary accident or will damage electronic equipment. Suitable static discharge facilities should be used.

PME

The correct procedures for a PME installation will vary depending on the individual circumstances. You must get professional advice for you particular installation. The RSGB EMC Committee leaflet number 7 on the RSGB EMC web site should be studied.

Older houses were fed with an electricity supply cable with a metal armoured sheath that was well earthed at the electricity sub-station. The house earth was bonded to that sheath. More recently, PME practice is used which does not use metal armoured cable and there is no earth connection. Instead, the house earth wiring is bonded to the supply neutral, which is earthed at the sub-station. In normal circumstances that is perfectly acceptable.

However, if the neutral line is broken between the house and the sub-station then there is no return path for the current and the neutral will rise, possibly to the full phase (live) voltage. Consequently the earth wire will also rise to the same voltage, as will all metal cased, earthed appliances. For that reason, metalwork in the house, such as water / central heating pipes, are also bonded (called cross-bonded) to the neutral / earth point so that all exposed metalwork is at an equal potential.

The danger comes when a real earth is introduced, the RF earth in the shack. All the current from the house, and, depending on the location of the ruptured neutral, half the street, will now try to flow down the RF earth. If this is via chance connections in the earth wire in 3-core flex and feeder braid connections, then either there is a severe risk of overheating and fire or a fatal shock if the RF plug is removed from the transceiver (now live) while the feeder is still earthed.

The normal recommendation is that the RF earth must be bonded directly to the supply bonding point by a substantial cable of at least 10mm^2. To avoid that compromising the EMC arrangements, that cross-bonding connection should be fitted with ferrite rings. A minimum of 20 turns is suggested. Due to the thickness of the cable, this may be 20 substantial ferrite tubes or small rings or, perhaps, two turns through 10 rings. You are reminded to take proper advice to see if you have a PME supply and what precautions are appropriate to your particular circumstances. This is not an issue to ignore and not one where one size fits all.

Sample Questions

There are three questions on safety in the Advanced exam:

Question	Syllabus Item
56	9a.1, 9a.2, 9a.3, 9a.4
57	9b.1, 9c.1, 9d.1
58	9e.1, 9f.1

a9a1-1
The main purpose of having a single master 'off' switch in the shack is to

A allow anybody in the house to be able to respond to a complaint of interference when the licensee may be absent

B simplify the procedure of having to switch many different supplies when starting and finishing a period of operations

C provide a single cable where a good filter may be fitted for EMC purposes rather than having to fit multiple filters

D have a known single point of cutting all power to the shack, except a ceiling mounted light, in case of an accident.

a9a2-1
All exposed metal surfaces must be earthed

A so the supply fuse or circuit breaker will 'blow' in the event of a fault occurring in the equipment

B in order to maintain the equi-potential environment required unless the house has a PME supply

C to prevent RF radiating from the casing of equipments and the resulting risk of interference

D to prevent the build up of static charges either from nylon carpets or induced by nearby thunderstorms.

a9a3-1

When unavoidably working on a live equipment you should

A wear an anti-static wrist band with a resistance to earth of not greater than 20Ω

B keep one hand clear of the equipment and earthed objects at all times

C display a notice on the shack door reading "Live working - No Entry"

D place the equipment concerned on an insulating rubber mat.

a9a4-1

Voltages higher than that of the mains supply are likely to be found

A in the power supply of a high power transistor RF amplifier

B in equipment utilising thermionic valves

C in a PME supply with a ruptured neutral

D at the fed end of end-fed antennas.

a9b1-1

When operating a special event station in tented accommodation and an extension cable to provide mains power, it is necessary to

A use a residual current protective device

B use circuit breakers in preference to wire fuses

C route the power supply cable well above head height

D provide additional filtering to avoid unwanted radiation.

a9c1-1

When fitting a transmitter in a vehicle, you should

A use one of the existing circuits to obtain power for the radio to avoid risk of interference

B identify a suitable power supply circuit that is only live once the engine has started

C route all RF cables well away from the vehicle wiring and electronic engine management systems

D fit a fuse in the existing lead from the battery negative terminal to the vehicle chassis.

a9d1-1

The HPA provides guidance of the field strength above which more detailed checks on exposure are required. The lowest level is

A 10 V/m

B 28 V/m

C 10 W/m²

D 28 W/m².

a9e1-1

Fitting a proprietary spark gap and discharge tube to the feeder to an HF dipole antenna should

A prevent the build up of damaging static charges

B avoid damage to the transceiver in the event of being struck by lightning

C permit a second receiver to be fitted to the antenna even while transmitting

D avoid the need to disconnect the transceiver during a thunderstorm.

a9f1-1

In a premises supplied using PME practice, the supply company will have connected the main earth point to

A the earthed outer sheath of the underground supply

B the neutral conductor at the point of entry to the premises

C an earth rod adjacent to the point of entry

D the mains water supply to the premises.

10. Morse code, Construction and Measurements

The Morse appreciation test is simply a practice at sending and receiving with the crib sheet available. You will send and receive some 20 - 30 characters, A - Z and 0 - 9, but no punctuation or procedural symbols. The speed is up to you and you can fill in corrections at the time or at the end, until all the errors have been corrected. Its purpose is simply to give you a modest understanding of what the code is. A sample piece of Morse is included here, which would normally be played to you.

The text is given in the Answers section at the end of the book.

INTERMEDIATE

Component identification, soldering and the colour code are assessed in the written exam as well as being part of the practical assessment. Components are shown as line drawings.

Soldering

The basis of soldering is the melting of the solder such that it adheres to the items, wire, tag or copper track. To do that the copper must be clean, free from grease, especially from fingers, and not oxidised. That means it must be cleaned just before soldering and touching the surfaces should be avoided.

Flux is required for good soldered joints. Its main purpose is to flow over the surfaces as they are heated to prevent oxidation. Some fluxes have a cleaning action but the aggressive ones sometimes used in plumbing must be avoided. Multicore solder has the flux within the solder.

Until recently, solder consisted of tin and lead but new rules require lead-free solder to be used commercially for health reasons. Existing equipment using leaded solder needs to be repaired using leaded solder. Similarly new lead-free items should be repaired with lead-free solder.

Not all metals will solder. Copper, brass, bronze, tin and zinc solder well. Some steels can be soldered but adhesion is poorer. Aluminium will not take conventional solder and oxidises very quickly. Special flux and aluminium solder can make a good job but it is not commonly required in amateur usage.

Connections to an aluminium case are made using a bolted on solder tag.

The soldering iron tip should be cleaned by wiping on a damp sponge and then 'tinned', that is given a light coat of solder to prevent the tip oxidising and to provide modest 'wetting' to allow good heat flow. Wires should be tinned to ease and speed soldering. Some components and circuit boards can be damaged by excess heat so the task should be performed reasonably quickly. Preparation, cleaning and tinning will ensure this is possible.

The solder should be seen to flow into the joint and smoothly thin out away from the joint. Any tendency to sit on the copper like a bubble with a sharp edge at the solder-metal boundary is indicative of non-adhesion, usually due to grease or dirt, or heating the solder but not the job. Good leaded solder joints will be shiny but poor joints, 'dry joints', will be dull in appearance. Unfortunately, lead-free solder gives a dull appearance even if the joint is perfectly good. Most faults in constructional projects turns out to be dry joints.

Colour code

The final item examined in the written paper, and also covered in the practical, is the resistor colour code. The code is given below and examples of how to convert the coloured bands found on resistors into actual values are given in **Fig 10.1**.

Black	0 (zero)
Brown	1
Red	2
Orange	3
Yellow	4
Green	5
Blue	6
Violet	7
Grey	8
White	9
Gold	Divide by 10

The resistor colour code.

Silver	10%
Gold	5%
Red	2%
Brown	1%

Resistor tolerance codes (4th band, see Fig 10.1).

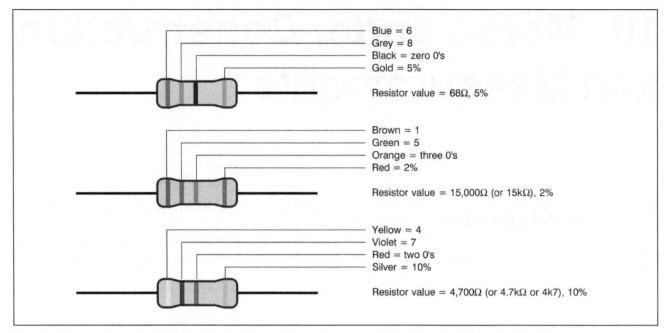

Fig 10.1. Examples of resistors, showing how to convert the coloured bands into actual values.

Sample Questions

Sections 10a.1 to 10c.1 are assessed in the written paper; sections 10d, 10e and 10f are covered as a practical exercise.

Question	Syllabus Item
44	10a.1 10b.1 10b.2 10b.3 10b.4 10b.5
45	10c.1

i10a1-1

The item in the drawing is a

A   crystal
B   resistor
C   capacitor
D   transistor.

i10b1-1

Soldering a wire to the copper track of a circuit board will

A   melt the wire onto the copper board
B   glue the wire onto the copper board
C   melt both the wire and a bit of the copper board
D   melt another metal onto the wire and the copper board.

i10b2.1

Most solders contain a flux, its purpose is to

A   hold the wire in place while the iron is applied and the solder sets
B   improve the heat transfer from the iron to the wire
C   prevent the copper surfaces oxidising as they get hot
D   coat the joint to reduce the risk of subsequent corrosion.

i10b3-1

Which metal CANNOT be soldered using a tin or tin / lead based solder?

A   Brass.
B   Aluminium.
C   Zinc.
D   Copper.

i10b4-1

Why is it advisable to 'tin' the wires prior to soldering the joint?

A   The solder is unlikely to adhere to both surfaces in one operation.
B   Tinning ensures the wires are clean and ready to be soldered.
C   The tinning ensures better heat conduction to the joint.
D   Tinning avoids the flux coming into contact with the bare copper.

i10b5-1

Many construction faults are caused by

A   dry joints
B   wet joints
C   flux insulating the joint
D   overheating the joints.

i10c1-1

A resistor is held up to show the bands gold, green, red, red.

A   The actual value will be within 10% of that indicated.
B   The resistance will be greater than $1M\Omega$.
C   The resistance is $225k\Omega$.
D   The tolerance is given as 2%.

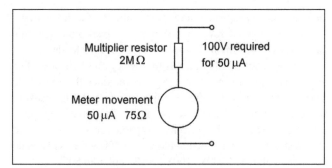

Fig 10.2. An analogue voltmeter.

ADVANCED

Analogue multimeters

The key point to appreciate is that an analogue multimeter is a sensitive micro-ammeter with resistors to determine the required voltage or current range.

Fig 10.2 shows a meter of basic range 50μA and an internal resistance of 75Ω. To make a 0 - 100V voltmeter a series resistance of R = V/I = 100/(50×10⁻⁶) = 2MΩ is needed so that 100V causes 50μA to flow, leading to a full scale deflection on the meter. The 75Ω in the meter is low compared to the 2MΩ resistor so the error in ignoring it is much less than the intrinsic accuracy of the meter movement. That is around 3% for a typical device, more for a cheap offering and 1% for top quality devices.

An ammeter requires a shunt, a parallel resistor to take the bulk of the current as shown in **Fig 10.3**. The voltage across the meter movement will be V= I×R = 50×10⁻⁶ × 75 = 3·75mV. For a 10A meter the shunt resistance will be R = V/I = 3·75/10 mΩ = 0·375mΩ. It essential the current flows direct through the shunt and the meter connections do not carry the high current. Under no circumstances should the

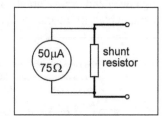

Fig 10.3. An analogue ammeter.

high current shunt circuit contain a switched contact since any contact resistance or momentary loss of contact will force the 10A current through the meter movement resulting in instant destruction.

The calculation can be simplified to:

$$R_{shunt} = R_{meter}\left(\frac{I_{meter}}{I_{shunt}}\right)$$

provided the current being measured is at least 50 times the meter movement current.

Switching off and storage

A bare meter movement is supplied with its contacts shorted. This is to 'damp' the movement. If the needle is moved by vibration a current will be induced in the coil which will counteract the movement and result in a much more sluggish response. This will minimise the chance of damage.

A multimeter often has some additional resistance in the meter circuit and the damping effect is much less evident when the meter prods are shorted. More important is the risk of

forgetting to set the right range when first used on any one occasion. For this reason the meter should be stored in the 'off' position if there is one or the highest voltage range available. This will avoid the 'excitement' of trying to measure a voltage when the meter has been left on a current range.

Effect on the circuit

Analogue meters draw current from the circuit under test. If that current is a significant proportion of the current normally flowing in that circuit then the addition of the meter will substantially affect the circuit, possibly upsetting biasing and causing other undesirable effects. At the very least, the reading will be wrong.

Fig 10.4 shows a 10V meter based on a 50μA movement measuring the output of a potential divider. Calculation of the actual voltages, including the meter in the circuit calculation, will show that the meter and R2 have the same resistance, the parallel combination is halved and the output voltage is 3·3V instead of the 5V expected. The meter will read 3·3V.

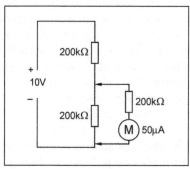

Fig 10.4. The effect of a meter on the circuit under test.

Wavemeters

A wavemeter is a tuned circuit, diode and a sensitive meter movement. In effect, it is a crystal set with a meter instead of an earpiece. Unfortunately it is too insensitive in today's crowded bands to be of much use. A signal that will register on the wavemeter, such as a harmonic, is already far too strong to be acceptable.

A heterodyne wavemeter has a crystal oscillator, allowing the signal under test to beat with the crystal and give a much more accurate indication of frequency. A crystal calibrator is similar but simply generates known frequencies. Digital division of, say, a 10MHz crystal can give harmonics at 1MHz intervals. Further division (by 10) will give 100kHz intervals, useful for many of the amateur bands. A 10kHz output may not have strong harmonics in the MHz region and the harmonics will be too closely spaced to be confident which harmonic is being heard. The division ratio should be set to the lowest value (ie highest frequency) that will still give a harmonic at the relevant band edge or frequency concerned.

Frequency counters

The frequency counter requires a single clean signal of sufficient strength. Off-air works only close to the transmitter. Typically it counts cycles for a set time. A 1 second 'gate' will give 1Hz resolution, whereas a 1mS gate will only give 1kHz resolution. Accuracy depends on the accuracy of the gate time, not the length of the gate time or the number of digits in the display.

A crystal with 5ppm initial accuracy and aging at 5ppm per year may be up to 20ppm out after 3 years. That is 200Hz error in a 10MHz signal or almost 3kHz in the 2m band.

Both the heterodyne wavemeter and the frequency coun-

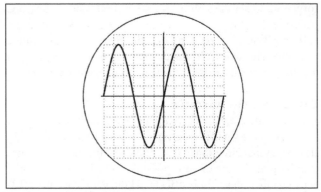

Fig 10.5. Oscilloscope display of two cycles of a sine wave.

ter can be checked against a standard frequency transmission. The standard frequency is tuned in to on a receiver and a local signal from the wavemeter or frequency counter clock set to zero beat with the off-air standard. The zero beat, or beating a low note equally each side of the test signal is more reliable than simply using the off-air signal to calibrate the receiver dial and then using the receiver as a measuring instrument. Signal and filter bandwidths will conspire to limit the accuracy achieved.

The counter will respond to the fundamental signal, not a harmonic or spurious signal unless they are stronger than the fundamental. If so the display could be corrupted and meaningless.

Oscilloscopes

The oscilloscope uses a sawtooth waveform to move a trace across a CRT (or PC) screen at a linear rate, drawing a horizontal line. The signal under test moves the trace vertically and the sawtooth, the timebase, adjusted to display one or two cycles across the screen as shown in **Fig 10.5**. As shown, a single cycle occupies 6 divisions. At 10µS per division this is 60µS per cycle and the frequency is $1/(60 \times 10^{-6})$, which is 16,667Hz. Of course, the instrument cannot be read to that accuracy and the timebase will have its own tolerances. 16·7kHz is the best that can be expected and in many cases one could only really say it's about midway between 16 and 17kHz.

RF power measurement

True measurement of RF power requires expensive instruments and utilises a *bolometer*. This measures the heating effect as a temperature rise and gives a true power reading. Most bolometers measure in the mW range and must be preceded by an accurate attenuator capable of handling the power. For our purposes it is sufficient to assume the waveform is sinusoidal and measure the voltage across a 50Ω dummy load. This may be done using as oscilloscope or a diode probe, shown in **Fig 10.6**. Both

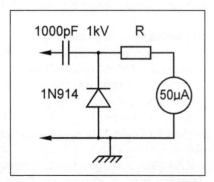

Fig 10.6. The diode probe rectifies the RF signal and produces a DC voltage.

devices record the peak voltage (remembering the diode drop).

Power is V^2/R for rms voltages; for peak voltages, this becomes $V^2/2R$, which is simply $V^2/100$ for 50Ω loads.

The licence always quotes the *peak power* allowed. For FM this is the same as the average power since the amplitude is constant. For AM and SSB this is a bit harder to measure and does require an oscilloscope. The definition of pep (peak envelope power) is the power averaged over one RF cycle at the crest of the modulation envelope. For 400W this will equate to a peak voltage of 200V. 100W is 100Vpk into 50Ω.

Some power meters have a peak reading capability. Typically they are a diode probe with a capacitor to hold the highest voltage reached as the RF level varies.

SWR meters

The Standing Wave Ratio was described in Section 5. Most SWR meters are some form of directional coupler. That is, they will couple or transfer a small sample of the power to a metering circuit only if the power is flowing in a particular direction.

There are two key types. One utilises a voltage potential divider and a current transformer in a 'T' circuit so the phases of the coupled voltage and current add in one arm of the T and cancel in the other. By that means the direction of power flow can be determined. **Fig 10.7** shows the rudiments of the circuit. The other method utilises a sense wire inside the coaxial feeder, relying on the fact that the power induced in the sense wire is also directional and can be measured using diode probes. This is shown in **Fig 10.8**.

In both cases, it is possible to use two meters each reading power and using a graph to determine the SWR. A neater solution places both meters in the same housing so the meters

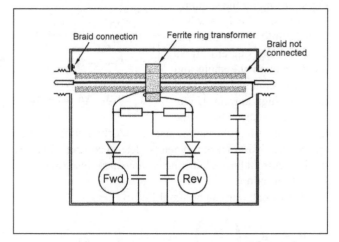

Fig 10.7. SWR meter using a current transformer.

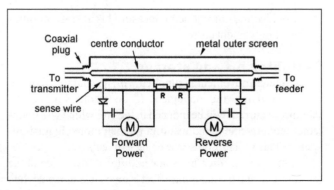

Fig 10.8. SWR meter using a sense wire.

indicate power on a scale, but also arranges that the meter needles cross in the centre of the scale-plate and the SWR is indicated by the point they cross. Less expensive meters have a sensitivity adjustment, which is set to read 100% in the forward direction and then switch the one meter to read reverse power as a proportion, allowing the scale to be marked as SWR directly. These meters are a useful indication, but should not be considered to be a calibrated instrument.

Sample Questions

The Advanced examination has four questions on measurements:

Question	Syllabus Item
59	10a.1
60	10b.1, 10b.2
61	10c.1
62	10d.1, 10e.1

a10a1-1
A 1mA meter has a 30Ω internal resistance and is to be used as a 5A meter in a power supply unit. The shunt resistor should have a resistance of
A   1mΩ
B   5mΩ
C   6mΩ
D   30mΩ.

a10a1-2
The meters in the drawing are correctly set to an appropriate range except that meter 3 has been left on 10mA DC. What will be the reading on meter 4?
A   0mA.
B   0·67mA.
C   1·0mA.
D   1·5mA.

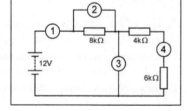

a10b1-1
A 3·5MHz transmitter is believed to have a third harmonic. A suitable device to check this is
A   an absorption wavemeter
B   an oscilloscope
C   a frequency counter
D   an HF receiver.

a10b2-1
A 10MHz crystal reference has an original accuracy of 5ppm and ages at 5ppm per year. A year later it is used to check a 10MHz USB transmitter. It is estimated the reference can be compared with the receiver to an accuracy of 100Hz and the transmitter can then be relied on to the nearest 100Hz within a month of calibration. The bandwidth of the transmitter is limited to 500Hz, mode J2B. What is the lowest frequency is it safe to transmit in the 10MHz amateur band that day without risking being out of band?
A   10,000·3kHz.
B   10,000·8kHz.
C   10,100·3kHz.
D   10,103·0kHz.

a10c1-1
An oscilloscope timebase is set to 1mS per division and the Y-axis to 10mV per division. The signal in the diagram is approximately
A   500Hz   20mV rms
B   500Hz   30mV rms
C   2kHz   20mV rms
D   2kHz   30mV rms.

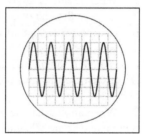

a10d1-1
A peak reading diode probe is used to measure the transmitter RF output into a dummy load. The probe indicates 12V. What is the output power?
A   0·8W.
B   1·2W.
C   1·4W.
D   2·9W.

a10e1-1
The switch in the diagram is likely to be labelled
A   hi-lo
B   on-off
C   + −
D   fwd-rev.

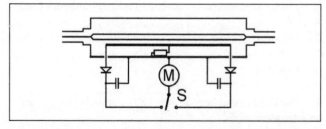

11. Sample Papers

1. The Foundation licence permits the holder to use amateur radio anywhere in
A the United Kingdom
B Europe
C the Commonwealth
D countries agreeing to T/R 61-01.

2. When identifying your station you should
A do so at the end of each 'over'
B use the same type of transmission as used for sending your message
C change frequency to the calling channel
D listen carefully and ask if the frequency is clear.

3. When another amateur is using your radio and is identifying using your callsign, then
A you can leave him or her alone since they have their own licence
B you must supervise them because they are using your equipment
C you must supervise them because they are using your callsign
D it is sufficient for you to listen to what they are saying on another receiver.

4. If you move house then your licence requires you to
A add the suffix '/A' to your callsign until you have a replacement licence
B immediately notify the Post Office of your new address
C immediately notify Ofcom of your new address
D ensure your new details are published in the call book.

5. The transmitted power on 10230MHz should not exceed
A 1W
B 1W e.r.p.
C 10W
D 10W e.r.p.

6. The Foundation licence does NOT permit you to transmit on a frequency of
A 1·950MHz
B 7·350MHz
C 14·150MHz
D 18·125MHz.

7. A long length of wire to a transmitter in the garden has a resistance of half an ohm (0·5Ω). When the transmitter is drawing 3A the voltage dropped in the wire will be
A 0·5V
B 1·5V
C 3V
D 3·5V.

8. The symbol shown in the drawing is the symbol for
A a resistor
B a lamp
C an antenna
D an earth.

9. The frequency range required for speech communication purposes is about
A 100Hz - 5kHz
B 100Hz - 15kHz
C 300Hz - 3kHz
D 300Hz - 15kHz.

10. Frequencies just above the 2 metre (144 - 146MHz) amateur band are used by
A Broadcasting
B Mobile (except aeronautical mobile)
C Radionavigation Satellite
D Space Operations and Space Research.

11. Which drawing represents a frequency modulated carrier wave?
A Drawing A
B Drawing B
C Drawing C
D Drawing D.

12. Use of the wrong antenna on a transmitter
A will only affect the strength of the transmitted signal
B may result in the wrong frequency being transmitted
C will affect the way the carrier is modulated
D may result in damage to the transmitter.

13. Which stage of the receiver block diagram demodulates the wanted signal?
A Stage 1.
B Stage 2.
C Stage 3.
D Stage 4.

14 The plug in the diagram is known as a
A N-type plug
B BNC plug
C PL259 plug
D RS232 plug.

15. Which type of antenna has an omni-directional coverage?
A Horizontal dipole.
B 5/8λ ground plane.
C Yagi.
D End fed.

16. What should be used to connect the centre of a horizontal dipole antenna to a coaxial cable feeder?
A A balun.
B An SWR meter.
C An ATU.
D A low pass filter.

17. At which point in the diagram would you expect the radio signal to be the weakest?
A Point A.
B Point B.
C Point C.
D Point D.

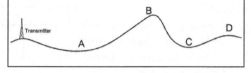

18. The bottom of the ionosphere is
A just above the ground
B at a height of 8km
C at a height of 70km
D at a height of 400km.

19. Interference to television signals is likely to be caused by
A birds sitting on the TV aerial
B a mains powered clock radio
C an amateur radio transmitter
D the TV remote control unit.

20. Which type of transmission is the LEAST likely to cause interference?
A Frequency modulation.
B Single sideband.
C Morse (CW).
D Amplitude modulation.

21. A source of advice on how to deal with a complaint of interference is the
A police
B British Broadcasting Corporation
C Radio Society of Great Britain
D local council.

22. The calling frequency in the 2-metre amateur band (144 - 146MHz) is
A 144· 500MHz
B 144· 750MHz
C 145· 250MHz
D 145· 500MHz.

23. The difference between a CQ on HF SSB and a CQ call on VHF FM is that
A the FM call is short and repeated once if required
B the FM call is long but only repeated once
C the SSB call is long but only repeated once
D the SSB call is short but repeated several times if required

24. While listening on 2 metres you overhear another amateur discussing the latest pop music and playing sample pieces to a few amateurs he is in contact with. You should:
A join the group and comment on the music if it interests you
B call in to the group and object to the playing of music
C find another frequency and talk to somebody else
D key the microphone PTT to transmit over the top of the music

25. In a mains plug the NEUTRAL wire is coloured
A black
B brown
C grey
D blue.

26. If you find a fellow amateur lying on the floor holding a piece of equipment, you should
A switch off the power before doing anything else
B pull his hand away from the equipment
C pull the equipment away from his hand
D turn the casualty into the recovery position and go for help

INTERMEDIATE

1. The callsign G8SDZ belongs to someone holding a
A Foundation Licence
B early Novice Licence
C Intermediate licence
D Full Licence.

2. If you are at the house of a Foundation licensee and using their equipment you
A must give their callsign and obey the terms of their licence
B may use your own callsign and obey the terms of your licence
C may use your callsign, but only if the Foundation licensee is supervising
D must obey the terms of your licence and give the Foundation callsign.

3. A Temporary Location is
A a fixed location that does not have a postal address
B the house of a friend provided you are not intending to stay overnight
C a hotel where you are staying provided it does not exceed three months
D the field, park, house or hotel where you are located provided it is not your property.

4. You may operate from a vessel ONLY if it is
A upstream of a lock or barrier to prevent tidal flow
B inland on a lake, loch, or upstream river
C on the landward side of the low water line
D a houseboat that is your main station address.

5. A friend who lives on a hill allows you to put your main transmitter at his house for you to operate by remote control. This is allowed by your licence provided
A your friend is also a licensed amateur
B your friend is at his home when you are operating
C you control your radio by internet or by amateur radio
D you only control your radio by a radio link in an amateur band.

6. What time period is given in the licence for checking you station does not cause interference?
A From time to time.
B Every three months.
C Every six months.
D Annually.

7. You must immediately inform Ofcom if you
A change your name
B replace your transmitter
C cause interference to television reception
D are out of the country from more than a month.

8. What is the status of the 3·5 to 3·8MHz amateur band?
A Secondary.
B Primary.
C Primary. Shared with other services.
D Primary. Available on the basis of non-interference with other services outside the UK.

9. What maximum transmit power on 431·5MHz may be used by an Intermediate amateur in Wales?
A The same power as an Intermediate amateur anywhere in England.
B The same power as an Intermediate amateur anywhere in Scotland.
C The licence limits the power to a maximum of 32W erp.
D The maximum permitted power on that frequency is 50W.

10. How many nano-Farads are there in a milli-Farad?
A 100.
B 1000.
C 1000,000.
D 1000,000,000.

11. What power is supplied by the battery in the diagram?
A 1·25W.
B 2·5W.
C 5W.
D 10W.

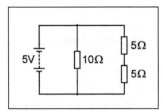

12. An inductor stores
A current in the field between the plates
B current in the field surrounding the coil
C energy in the field between the plates
D energy in the field surrounding the coil.

13. The ratio of the potential difference across a capacitor to the current through it is the
A capacitance in farads
B reactance in ohms
C dissipation in watts
D impedance in henries.

14 If the capacitor in the drawing is charged when the switch S is closed, the energy will flow into the inductor at a rate determined by
A the amount of energy in the capacitor
B only the value of the inductor
C only the value of the capacitor
D the value of both components.

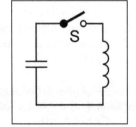

15. A transformer has 1000 turns on its primary winding and 200 turns on its secondary winding and is fed from an AC supply. The output from the secondary will be
A AC at a higher voltage than the primary
B AC at a lower voltage than the primary
C DC at a higher voltage than the primary
D DC at a lower voltage than the primary.

16. What is the purpose of resistors R1 and R2 in the circuit diagram?
A Conduct the input signal to the base of the transistor.
B Provide the correct biasing for the transistor.
C Prevent any DC voltage on the input from affecting the transistor.
D Set the gain of the transistor to the desired value.

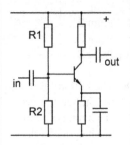

17. The circuits in a radio receiver are being adjusted for a maximum output and a meter is connected to the output to display the reading. The meter should be
A an analogue meter so the changes are easy to see
B a digital meter so the changes are easy to see
C an analogue meter to give an accurate figure
D a digital meter to give an accurate figure.

18. A transmitter uses a mixer to help produce the desired frequency. The two inputs are at 2·7MHz and 4·4MHz. The mixer output will be
A a signal at 3·55MHz
B nothing at all because the inputs are different
C two signals, one at 1·7MHz and the other at 7·1MHz
D a signal varying between 2·7 and 4·4MHz.

19. Which methods of modulation (modes) are such that, for the same input, one always has twice the bandwidth of the other?
A AM and FM.
B FM and CW.
C CW and SSB.
D SSB and AM.

20. The MOST SERIOUS effect of excessive amplitude into an AM modulator is that the
A received audio will be too loud
B transmitted bandwidth will be excessive
C received audio will be distorted and hard to understand
D transmitter will drift off frequency.

21. The filter which has the frequency response shown in the drawing is a
A high pass filter
B low pass filter
C band pass filter
D high stop filter.

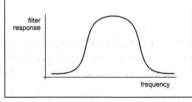

22. The block marked 'X' in the block diagram of a radio receiver is the
A   IF Amplifier
B   RF amplifier
C   Mixer
D   Demodulator.

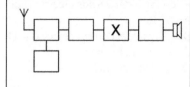

23. The wanted frequency is selected by tuned circuits in the
A   mixer
B   IF amplifier
C   demodulator
D   audio amplifier.

24. The AGC signal produced by the detector (demodulator) is used to
A   feed an audio signal to the audio amplifier
B   vary the frequency of the local oscillator to ensure exact tuning
C   ensure the mixer is operating on the correct sideband
D   set the gain of the IF and sometimes the RF amplifier.

25. The characteristic impedance of a coaxial feeder is determined by the
A   standing wave ratio present on the feeder
B   value of the impedance connected to the far end of the feeder
C   diameter and spacing of the feeder conductors
D   length of the feeder in terms of the wavelength of the signal.

26. If an antenna is used on a frequency other than that for which it was designed then
A   the signal coming up the feeder will be lost as heat instead of being radiated
B   some of the energy from the transmitter will be reflected back down the feeder
C   the standing waves will prevent the signal from reaching the antenna
D   the transmitted signal is likely to drift in frequency, risk ing damage to the transmitter.

27. Which antenna described below will allow equal reception of signals from any direction?
A   A dipole mounted vertically.
B   A dipole mounted horizontally.
C   A Yagi mounted vertically.
D   A Yagi mounted horizontally.

28. It is noticed that some years have better HF radio propagation than others and that this year seems to be a peak and propagation is beginning to decline. How long is it likely to be before there is another peak?
A   Next year.
B   Six years time.
C   Eleven years time.
D   In about fifteen years.

29. The phenomenon know as ducting often
A   reduces the range of HF signals
B   traps HF signals in the ionosphere
C   causes a temporary loss of VHF communication
D   extends the range of VHF propagation.

30. A second-hand Yagi antenna is seen for sale at a rally. The driven element is 125cm long. The Yagi is intended for use on a frequency around
A   80MHz
B   120MHz
C   145MHz
D   240MHz.

31. The fact that a new piece of electronic equipment is 'CE' marked as complying with the European EMC immunity requirements means that
A   it has been made to a reasonable standard of immunity, but may still suffer from strong amateur transmissions
B   it will not be affected by any amateur transmission that comply with the requirements of the amateur licence
C   if interference does occur then the owner is entitled to have it replaced under the guarantee
D   it must be installed by a properly trained person to maintain its guarantee.

32. An investigation discovers that the mains wiring in an amateur's house is also carrying sufficient RF signal to cause interference to other equipment. A sensible next step is to
A   fit filters in the mains leads of the affected equipments
B   fit a filter in the mains lead to the transmitter
C   connect the casing of the transmitter to the mains earth lead
D   fit an ATU in the mains supply to the transmitter.

33. It is found that a VHF SSB transmitter can be heard on a clock radio. Tests reveal that the tuning of the radio or of the transmitter has little or no effect on the pickup. This suggests that the cause of the problem might be
A   RF signals picked up by the clock radio antenna
B   direct pickup inside the clock radio
C   inadequate filtering of the transmitter output
D   harmonics generated in the transmitter.

34. VHF transmissions are causing interference to an amateur's own television and may be due to RF leaking down the transmitter mains lead or by the radiated signal being picked up by the house wiring and TV mains lead. To find out which, a suitable test would be to
A   transmit into a dummy load
B   fit a ferrite ring on the mains lead to the TV
C   use an RF filter which plugs into the mains socket and plug the TV into the filter.
D   unplug the aerial lead to the TV while the transmission is in progress.

35. Further information on dealing with difficult interference cases is available from
A   British Telecom
B   the local council
C   the RSGB
D   your local electricity supplier.

36. The reply to a CQ call is 'QRZ' and the speaker's call sign. You should
A   give your call sign again
B   offer to find a clear frequency
C   report the strength of the received signal
D   apologise and call CQ on a different frequency.

37. A personal computer and interface or sound card would NOT normally be used for transmitting
A   slow-scan television
B   amateur packet
C   SSB voice
D   data.

38. The callsign W2AB indicates that the amateur is calling from
A   United States
B   Australia
C   Canada
D   Japan.

39 The phenomenon known as Doppler shift is noticeable when
A   on an HF ionospheric contact
B   mobile on VHF
C   ducting is affecting propagation
D   operating via a satellite.

40. It is advisable to have a well ventilated work area when soldering because
A   the air flow allows the solder to cool more quickly
B   fumes from the flux can irritate the nasal passages
C   excess solder can be easily flicked out the window
D   the cooler air helps prevent the build up of static charges.

41. When drilling, it is helpful if the position to drill is marked by a
A   felt tip pen
B   scriber
C   centre punch
D   ruler.

42. The real reason for wearing a tool belt or similar item when working up a ladder is that
A   it makes dropping a tool much less likely
B   it saves frequent trips up and down the ladder
C   the tools are kept clean
D   the extra weight will help stabilise the ladder.

43. Which device will normally give the best protection against receiving a dangerous electric shock?
A   A fuse.
B   A residual current device (RCD).
C   A circuit breaker.
D   A PME supply.

44. What is the component shown in the drawing?
A   A diode.
B   A capacitor.
C   A crystal.
D   A transistor.

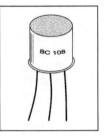

45. A resistor has four coloured bands, yellow, purple, gold, gold. Its resistance and tolerance is
A   4·7Ω 5%
B   47Ω 5%
C   4·7Ω 10%
D   47Ω 10%.

ADVANCED

1.   The call sign MM0XYZ/MM is heard calling CQ, the person calling
A   is not giving a correctly formatted call sign
B   has an address in Scotland but is at sea
C   is Scottish but currently elsewhere on the UK mainland
D   is on a vessel but could also be on an inland river or waterway.

2.   You are in communication with JA2CZ and are requested to QSY by a station having a non-amateur callsign claiming to be involved in disaster communication. You should
A   ignore the request because you may not respond to non-amateurs on amateur frequencies
B   report the station to the intruder watch service via the RSGB
C   comply with the request because non-amateur stations may legitimately be heard on amateur bands in disaster situations
D   challenge the station to give a proper amateur call sign.

3.   To supervise a foreign amateur from a CEPT country using your station during a temporary visit, you must hold
A   any UK amateur licence
B   at least an Intermediate licence
C   a Full licence
D   a Full licence and a CEPT Harmonised Amateur Radio Examination Certificate (HAREC).

4.   In order to operate amateur radio while on a cruise ship at sea you must
A   be in UK territorial waters
B   keep a log of all the transmissions made
C   ensure the ship's master is aware of your activities
D   have the written permission of the ship's master.

AMATEUR RADIO EXAM SECRETS

5. The rules to be complied with when operating abroad as a temporary visitor to a CEPT signatory country are
A as set out in your licence because it is also a CEPT licence
B those of the host country even if they are contrary to the terms of your UK licence
C only those which both your UK licence and the host country licence permits
D those applicable to the ITU region in which the host country is situated.

6. When tuning round you hear a Canadian amateur callsign on a frequency of 5·269MHz. Which statement below is correct?
A You may reply to him on that frequency.
B You should not continue to listen to that station.
C You should quickly ask the station to QSY to a UK amateur frequency.
D You may continue to listen, but only reply on a UK amateur frequency.

7. Which statement below is correct?
A All UK licensees are limited to a power of 500mW on the radio link to control a remote control main transmitter, which may use the power shown in their schedule.
B Full licensees may use any power up to 400W on the remote control link, in those bands where the main transmitter may use 400W.
C When operating by remote control, the main transmitter power is limited to 25W.
D When operating by remote control, the link transmitter power is limited to 25W.

8. You are taking part in a controlled net in support of an event. You transmit at 11.00, 11.05, 11.08, 11.40, 11.46 and 12.15. To comply with your licence, what is the minimum number of times you are required to give your call sign?
A Three.
B Four.
C Five.
D Six.

9. The call sign of a licensee may be published, with or without the licensee's consent, if
A A complaint of interference has been made.
B Ofcom have determined that the station is causing interference.
C The licensee has refused to remedy a case of interference.
D The licence concerned has been revoked.

10. A requirement of transmission of a frequency of 5840MHz is that
A no interference shall be caused to ISM users
B transmissions should not be directed to satellites
C interference to stations outside the UK must not be caused
D transmit power is limited to 400W erp.

11. It is decided to limit the lowest setting of a volume control to 1% of maximum power. The control itself is a 10kΩ potentiometer. To achieve this a resistor is inserted between the lower connection of the potentiometer and the 0V line as shown in the diagram. The value of the resistor should be
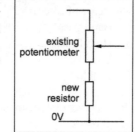
A 0·1kΩ
B 1kΩ
C 1·1kΩ
D 10kΩ.

12. A variable capacitor often has additional pre-set trimmer capacitors to set the tuning range, as shown in the circuit diagram. What is the MINIMUM capacitance of the circuit?
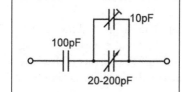
A 23pF.
B 30pF.
C 112pF.
D 130pF.

13. A coil is wound with a space between the turns. Squeezing the turns closer together will
A reduce the capacitance between the turns
B not affect the inductance
C increase the inductance
D reduce the inductance.

14 The dotted sine wave is
A lagging the solid one by 45°
B leading the solid one by 45°
C lagging the solid one by 125°
D leading the solid one by 125°.
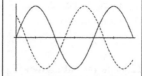

15. An 18·2μH coil and a resistor of 300Ω are connected in series. A current of 3mA at 3·5MHz is flowing through the circuit. What is the applied voltage?
A 0·9V.
B 0·96V.
C 1·5V.
D 2·1V.

16. A medium wave receiver is tuned to 909kHz and is receiving an AM signal having a bandwidth of 7kHz. A suitable Q-factor for the tuned circuit would be about
A 65
B 70
C 90
D 130.

17. A transformer has 960 turns on the primary and 64 turns on the secondary. The mains input is 240V rms. The load on the secondary is equivalent to a 2Ω resistor. What current is drawn from the mains assuming no losses in the transformer?
A 0·5A.
B 1A.
C 6·4A.
D 8A.

18. A filter has the frequency/amplitude response shown in the graph. What type of filter is it?

A   Band pass.
B   High Pass.
C   Low pass.
D   Notch.

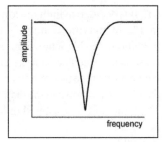

19. A power of 43dBm means 43dB relative to 1mW, that is a power of

A   2W
B   4·3W
C   20W
D   43W.

20. The diagram shows a P-N junction and a current limiting resistor. The potential difference across the junction is about

A   0V
B   0·7V
C   5V
D   10V.

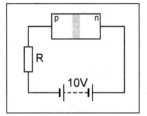

21. What configuration is the transistor amplifier in the circuit diagram?

A   Emitter follower.
B   Common emitter.
C   Common base.
D   Common collector.

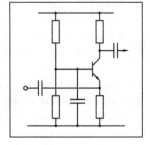

22. The circuit shown is part of a stabilised power supply. What device would be required in box X?

A   A series pass transistor.
B   An IC voltage regulator.
C   A ripple filter.
D   A Zener diode.

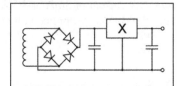

23. What component part of a transmitter would have an output called "out of lock"?

A   Automatic level control.
B   Frequency synthesiser.
C   Full break-in keying.
D   Standing wave detection circuit.

24. A modulator produces an output from 8·900MHz to 8·903MHz where 8·900MHz represents 0Hz audio. This is mixed with a VFO centred on 5·25MHz to produce outputs in the 20m and 80m amateur bands. The actual frequencies of the above arrangement will be

A   3·650 to 3·653MHz and 14·150 to 14·153MHz
B   3·650 to 3·647MHz and 14·150 to 14·153MHz
C   3·650 to 3·653MHz and 14·150 to 14·147MHz
D   3·650 to 3·647MHz and 14·150 to 14·147MHz.

25. The peak deviation of an FM modulated signal will occur when the audio input

A   is at a maximum instantaneous positive voltage
B   is at its maximum audio frequency
C   leads to a modulation index greater than 1
D   causes the depth of modulation to reach 100%.

26. The use of speech processing will

A   increase the peak to average signal level ratio
B   reduce the peak to average signal level ratio
C   prevent the peak power exceeding the 400W limit
D   allow a smaller heat sink or fan for the same output power.

27. Chirp is an effect often associated with

A   RF feedback into the modulator stage
B   poor voltage regulation of the oscillator
C   inadequate screening of the VFO
D   keying the output stage of the transmitter.

28. To reduce the risk of radiating harmonics and unwanted mixer products in an HF receiver it is common to use a

A   high pass filter
B   low pass filter
C   band pass filter
D   band stop filter.

29. The MOST LIKELY effect of over-driving an external power amplifier is that

A   transmissions will splatter into adjacent frequencies
B   harmonics of the transmit frequency will be radiated
C   the loading on the base transmitter will become unstable
D   frequency stability will be impaired, particularly on speech peaks.

30. The signal to noise ratio given in the specification of a receiver will

A   depend on the level of RF noise present at the antenna
B   depend on the level of signal at the antenna
C   indicate the amount of noise generated within the receiver
D   set the 'S0' level indicated on the signal strength meter.

31. The signal from the Beat Frequency Oscillator (BFO) is normally fed in to the

A   first mixer
B   intermediate amplifier
C   detector
D   audio amplifier.

32. The gain of an IF amplifier is normally varied by changing the

A   biasing of the IF transistors
B   coupling in the IF transformers
C   collector load on the IF transistors
D   decoupling on the IF transistor's emitter.

33. A superhet receiver is tuned to 1·82MHz and has an IF of 460kHz. The image frequency of the receiver might be

A   0·90MHz
B   0·92MHz
C   1·36MHz
D   2·28MHz.

34. The device shown in the diagram is a
A product detector
B SWR indicator
C frequency discrim-
inator
D PLL out-of-lock
detector.

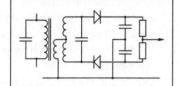

35. The RIT control on a transceiver will be of most use when
A operating on SSB whilst in a group of amateurs
B operating on SSB whilst in contact with a single amateur
C operating on FM whilst in a group of amateurs
D operating on FM whilst in contact with a single amateur.

36. An amateur inadvertently uses a short lead $\lambda/4$ long intended for use on an oscilloscope, where the characteristic impedance used is 75Ω. The lead is connected to a 50Ω dummy load. The impedance at the free end will be
A 37Ω
B 50Ω
C 75Ω
D 112Ω.

37. A quarter wave ground-plane antenna, mounted with the radiating element vertical has a feed impedance of approximately
A 25Ω
B 37Ω
C 50Ω
D 75Ω.

38. An HF dipole antenna is fitted with a trap in each half. The traps are about 5m from the centre of the dipole and overall length of the entire dipole is about 40m. At what frequency should the traps resonate?
A 3·6MHz.
B 7·1MHz.
C 14·2MHz.
D 29·0MHz.

39 The feeder of an existing installation is replaced with one having a lower loss. On checking the installation from in the shack, it should be observed that the SWR
A and return loss have increased
B has increased and the return loss reduced
C has reduced and the return loss increased
D and return loss have reduced.

40. It is decided to see if a good feeder and antenna system can be further improved by moving the ATU close to the antenna instead of in the shack. It should be found that the SWR at the transmitter is
A unchanged but the feeder SWR is reduced
B reduced and the feeder SWR is reduced
C unchanged and the feeder SWR is unchanged
D reduced and the feeder SWR is unchanged.

41. Communication with satellites often uses
A vertical polarisation
B slant polarisation
C horizontal polarisation
D circular polarisation.

42. Greatest range for a single hop is achieved by refraction in the
A D layer
B E layer
C F1 layer
D F2 layer.

43. Which of these parameters about the ionosphere will have the lowest frequency?
A MUF on a long path.
B MUF on a short path.
C Critical frequency.
D Gyro frequency.

44. Which amateur band falls in the TV video baseband?
A 6m.
B 10m.
C 30m.
D 80m.

45. Blocking is a phenomenon where
A a filter is used to remove an image channel in a receiver
B a strong constant signal close in frequency to the wanted signal, overloads the receiver input
C a transmission on the intermediate frequency of a receiver is picked up and interferes with the wanted signal
D a wanted signal is interrupted in time with the modulation envelope of an unwanted interfering signal.

46 RF entering an electronic device may be demodulated by
A the radio receiver section of the device
B any p-n junction in the device
C any tuned circuits close to the radio frequency concerned
D the loudspeaker and leads.

47. It is suspected the TV down lead is picking up an interfering HF signal. Which type of filter may be of use in curing this problem?
A A braid breaking filter.
B A low pass filter.
C A high pass filter.
D A band pass filter.

48. A particularly strong signal on 145MHz is causing interference to the FM broadcast band, notably 102·6MHz. A T-piece is used to connect a coaxial stub in parallel with the input to the domestic radio. The coaxial cable stub should be
A $\lambda/4$ at 102·6MHz with the free end shorted, inner to braid
B $\lambda/4$ at 145MHz with the free end shorted, inner to braid
C $\lambda/4$ at 145MHz with the free end open circuit and insulated
D $\lambda/2$ at 145MHz with the free end open circuit and insulated.

49. A competition station is using 400W fed to two stacked long Yagis with a total gain of 16dB. It is assumed that other equipment will have adequate immunity to field strengths up to 3V/m; that is achieved at a distance of about

A 30m
B 130m
C 300m
D 2·1km.

50. Balanced horizontal HF antennas tend to cause fewer EMC problems to neighbouring houses because

A house wiring is generally more susceptible to vertically polarised fields
B being balanced the horizontal fields will largely cancel out
C house wiring is unbalanced and less sensitive to balanced fields
D a balun at the antenna centre allows the coaxial cable feed to drop vertically away.

51. Your transmissions are causing interference to an old television nearby and the owner is complaining. You should

A suggest the old television is replaced with a new digital one since they are immune to interference
B see if a filter will cure the problem until digital switchover requires a new TV anyway
C tell the owner the TV is so old it is likely to suffer
D cease transmitting during peak TV viewing hours.

52. One advantage of sending a message by Packet radio is that

A the bandwidth required for transmission is much lower
B the recipient does not need to be present to receive the message
C non-amateurs are permitted to receive Packet messages
D the Packet system can translate typed messages into the recipient's own language.

53. You are confident you have correctly set the CTCSS tone and are getting into the new repeater but cannot hear any output at all. This may be because

A there is no one else around to reply
B some repeaters now use a 7·6MHz offset
C you are not waiting for the reset tone after transmitting
D you are not registered as a user on that repeater.

54. To identify a station as a Special Event station the callsign will normally

A begin with GB and then a number
B add the suffix /S to the normal callsign
C include the words 'special event'
D be taken from the G9 series not available to individual amateurs.

55. The amateur band plans state that

A FM should not be used on 10m
B SSB should not be used on 30m
C the 10MHz band may use upper or lower sideband operation
D the spot frequency 1·860MHz is exclusively used for direction finding beacons.

56. A particular safety hazard associated with valve power amplifier equipment is that

A some of the valves can get quite hot
B very high voltages are used which may be lethal
C the RF fields are higher than with similar transistorised equipments
D valves are less tolerant of high standing wave ratios.

57. The publication 'Reference Levels for UK Amateur Radio Bands' is produced by

A the Radio Society of Great Britain
B Ofcom
C the World Health Organisation
D the Health Protection Agency.

58. If the electricity supply is of a type known as 'PME' it is essential to

A remove the mains earth connection to transmitting equipment in the shack
B bond the RF earth to the main PME bonding point using substantial cable
C only use the supplied PME earth as an RF earth
D use isolated DC supplies only for the transmitting equipment.

59 A small 50µA movement meter is to be used as a voltmeter reading 0 - 15V DC. The meter coil has a resistance of 80Ω. What value resistor should be used and how should it be fitted?

A 15kΩ in series.
B 300kΩ in series.
C 15kΩ in parallel.
D 300kΩ in parallel.

60. The accuracy of a digital frequency meter is determined by the

A number of digits used for the frequency display
B the accuracy of the internal clock oscillator
C the gate time of the counting circuits
D frequency being measured.

61. The oscilloscope shown in the drawing has the time base set to 500µs/div and 10V/div. What is the frequency of the signal?

A 200Hz.
B 400Hz.
C 500Hz.
D 2kHz.

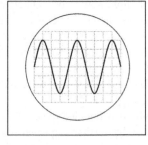

62. An RF thermocouple voltmeter is calibrated to read RMS voltages and indicates the key down CW output from a transmitter is 145V into the feeder. What power does this represent?

A 210W.
B 300W.
C 420W.
D 590W.

12. Answers

1. AMATEUR RADIO, AND 2. LICENSING CONDITIONS

Foundation
f1a1-1 D
f1a1-2 B
f2a1-1 A
f2a1-2 B
f2b1-1 D
f2b1-2 A
f2c1-1 D
f2c1-2 D
f2c2-1 A
f2c2-2 D
f2c3-1 A
f2c3-2 B
f2c4-1 A
f2c4-2 D
f2c5-1 A
f2c5-2 B
f2c6-1 B
f2c6-2 C
f2c7-1 B
f2c7-2 C
f2c8-1 B
f2c8-2 B
f2c9-1 C
f2c9-2 C

Intermediate
i1a1-1 B
i1a1-2 A
i2a1-1 B
i2a1-2 D
i2b1-1 B
i2b1-2 A
i2b2-1 C
i2b2-2 D
i2c1-1 B
i2c2-1 D
i2c2-2 C
i2c3-1 D
i2c3-2 C
i2c4-1 A
i2c4-2 D
i2d1-1 C
i2d1-2 B
i2e1-1 A
i2e1-2 D
i2f1-1 B
i2f2-1 C

i2f3-1 B
i2g1-1 C
i2g1-2 C
i2h1-1 D
i2h1-2 B
i2h2-1 C
i2h2-2 D

Advanced
a2a1-1 B
a2a1-2 A
a2b1-1 D
a2b1-2 B
a2c1-1 C
a2c1-2 C
a2d1-1 C
a2d1-2 D
a2e1-1 D
a2f1-1 C
a2f1-2 A
a2g1-1 B
a2g1-2 B
a2h1-1 B
a2h1-2 B
a2i1-1 B
a2i1-2 A
a2j1-1 B
a2j1-2 A

3. TECHNICAL BASICS

Foundation
f3a1-1 B
f3a1-2 B
f3b1-1 C
f3b1-2 A
f3b2-1 A
f3b2-2 D
f3b2-3 B
f3b3-1 B
f3b3-2 B
f3b3-3 A
f3b4-1 D
f3b5-1 A
f3b6-1 B
f3b7-1 A
f3b7-2 C
f3c1-1 C
f3c1-2 B
f3c2-1 B
f3c3-1 B
f3c3-2 B

Intermediate
i3a1-1 D
i3b1-1 A
i3b1-2 A
i3b1-3 C
i3b1-4 C
i3c1-1 B
i3d1-1 A
i3d2-1 C
i3d3-1 A
i3e1-1 A
i3e1-2 B
i3e1-3 C
i3f1-1 C
i3f1-2 C
i3f2-1 B
i3f3-1 B
i3f4-1 B
i3g1-1 C
i3g2-1 C
i3g3-1 A
i3h1-1 D
i3h2-1 A
i3h2-2 A
i3i1-1 C
i3i1-2 C
i3i1-3 A
i3i2-1 B
i3i3-1 B
i3i4-1 C
i3i5-1 D
i3i5-2 C
i3i5-3 C
i3i6-1 A
i3i7-1 B
i3i8-1 C
i3i8-2 A
i3j1-1 D
i3j2-1 C
i3j3-1 B
i3j4-1 B
i3j5-1 B

Advanced
a3a1-1 D
a3b1-1 B
a3c1-1 B
a3d1-1 C
a3e1-1 D
a3e2-1 C
a3e3-1 D
a3e4-1 B
a3e5-1 C

a3f1-1 B
a3f2-1 A
a3f3-1 B
a3f4-1 D
a3g1-1 B
a3g2-1 C
a3g3-1 C
a3h1-1 A
a3h1-2 B
a3h2-1 C
a3h3-1 B
a3i1-1 A
a3i2-1 A
a3i3-1 D
a3i3-2 C
a3i4-1 C
a3i5-1 C
a3i6-1 B
a3j1-1 A
a3j2-1 A
a3j3-1 C
a3k1-1 A
a3l1-1 C
a3m1-1 A
a3n1-1 B
a3n2-1 B
a3n3-1 C
a3n4-1 A
a3n5-1 A
a3n6-1 C
a3n7-1 D
a3n8-1 B
a3o1-1 C
a3p1-1 C
a3p2-1 D
a3p3-1 C

4. TRANSMITTERS AND RECEIVERS

Foundation
f4a1-1 B
f4b1-1 D
f4b2-1 B
f4b3-1 B
f4b4-1 C
f4b5-1 B
f4b6-1 B
f4c1-1 D
f4d1-1 B
f4d2-1 A

Intermediate

i4a1-1	C
i4a2-1	A
i4b1-1	B
i4b2-1	D
i4b3-1	B
i4b4-1	B
i4c1-1	A
i4d1-1	A
i4d2-1	D
i4d3-1	D
i4d4-1	B
i4d5-1	D
i4e1-1	B
i4e2-1	C
i4e3-1	C
i4e4-1	A
i4e5-1	D
i4f1-1	C
i4f2-1	C
i4g1-1	C
i4h1-1	A
i4i1-1	B
i4i1-2	A
i4i2-1	C
i4j1-1	D

Advanced

a4a1-1	B
a4b1-1	A
a4c1-1	C
a4d1-1	B
a4e1-1	C
a4f1-1	C
a4f2-1	D
a4f3-1	C
a4g1-1	C
a4g2-1	C
a4g3-1	A
a4g4-1	B
a4g5-1	B
a4h1-1	C
a4h2-1	B
a4h3-1	C
a4h4-1	C
a4h5-1	B
a4h6-1	B
a4i1-1	A
a4j1-1	D
a4j2-1	B
a4j3-1	B
a4k1-1	C
a4l1-1	D
a4m1-1	D
a4m2-1	B

a4n1-1	D
a4n2-1	B
a4o1-1	D
a4p1-1	A
a4q1-1	C
a4q1-2	B

5. FEEDERS AND ANTENNAS

Foundation

f5a1-1	A
f5a2-1	B
f5b1-1	B
f5b2-1	C
f5c1-1	D
f5c2-1	B
f5c3-1	D
f5c4-1	C
f5c5-1	B
f5d1-1	B
f5e1-1	A
f5e2-1	D
f5f1-1	C

Intermediate

i5a1-1	B
i5a2-1	B
i5a3-1	A
i5a4-1	D
i5a5-1	B
i5b1-1	C
i5c1-1	D
i5d1-1	C
i5e1-1	C
i5f1-1	B
i5f2-1	D
i5f3-1	A
i5f4-1	B
i5f5-1	D
i5g1-1	D

Advanced

a5a1-1	A
a5a2-1	B
a5a3-1	D
a5b1-1	C
a5c1-1	B
a5c2-1	B
a5c3-1	C
a5c4-1	B
a5c5-1	C
a5d1-1	D
a5d2-1	A
a5d3-1	A
a5e1-1	A

6. PROPAGATION

Foundation

f6a1-1	B
f6a2-1	C
f6a3-1	B
f5a4-1	B
f6a5-1	C
f6b1-1	A
f6b2-1	D

Intermediate

i6a1-1	D
i6a2-1	B
i6a3-1	C
i6a4-1	D
i6a5-1	A
i6a6-1	C
i6a7-1	B
i6a8-1	C

Advanced

a6a1-1	D
a6a2-1	A
a6b1-1	B
a6b2-1	B
a6b3-1	B
a6b4-1	C
a6b5-1	A
a6b6-1	D
a6b7-1	B
a6c1-1	A

7. EMC

Foundation

f7a1-1	A
f7a2-1	D
f7a3-1	B
f7a4-1	C
f7b1-1	B
f7b2-1	B
f7c1-1	D
f7c2-1	C
f7c3-1	B
f7d1-1	C

Intermediate

i7a1-1	C
i7a2-1	B
i7a3-1	B
i7b1-1	A
i7b2-1	C
i7b3-1	C
i7b4-1	B
i7b5-1	B

i7c1-1	A
i7c2-1	C
i7c3-1	A
i7c4-1	B
i7c5-1	B
i7c6-1	D
i7d1-1	A
i7d2-1	B
i7d3-1	B

Advanced

a7a1-1	A
a7a2-1	A
a7a3-1	A
a7a4-1	B
a7a5-1	B
a7a6-1	C
a7b1-1	C
a7b2-1	D
a7b3-1	B
a7b4-1	A
a7b5-1	A
a7c1-1	A
a7d1-1	C
a7e1-1	B
a7f1-1	C

8. OPERATING PRACTICES AND PROCEDURES

Foundation

f8a1-1	B
f8a2-1	B
f8a3-1	C
f8a4-1	D
f8a5-1	A
f8a6-1	D
f8b1-1	C
f8c1-1	A
f8d1-1	D

Intermediate

i8a1-1	A
i8b1-1	B
i8c1-1	B
i8d1-1	A
i8e1-1	D
i8e2-1	C
i8f1-1	B
i8f2-1	B
i8f3-1	A
i8f4-1	C
i8g1-1	B
i8g2-1	B
i8g3-1	D
i8g4-1	B

Advanced

a8a1-1	C
a8a1-2	A
a8b1-1	D
a8c1-1	B
a8d1-1	B
a8e1-1	C

9. SAFETY
Foundation

f9a1-1	B
f9a2-1	B
f9a3-1	B
f9a4-1	B
f9a5-1	A
f9a6-1	B
f9b1-1	B
f9c1-1	D
f9c2-1	C
f9c3-1	D
f9c4-1	A
f9c5-1	D
f9c6-1	C
f9d1-1	D

Intermediate

i9a1-1	B
i9b1-1	C
i9b2-1	A
i9b3-1	B
i9b4-1	C
i9b5-1	A
i9b6-1	C
i9c1-1	B
i9c2-1	B
i9c3-1	D
i9c4-1	D
i9d1-1	B
i9d2-1	B
i9d3-1	A
i9d4-1	B
i9e1-1	C
i9e2-1	C
i9e3-1	A

Advanced

a9a1-1	D
a9a2-1	A
a9a3-1	B
a9a4-1	B
a9b1-1	A
a9c1-1	C
a9d1-1	B
a9e1-1	A
a9f1-1	B

10. MORSE CODE, CONSTRUCTION AND MEASUREMENTS

Foundation
The sample text reads:
M3HKB DE 2E0NFK
I AM USING AN FT290
TRANSCEIVER

Intermediate

i10a1-1	A
i10b1-1	D
i10b2-1	C
i10b3-1	B
i10b4-1	B
i10b5-1	A
i10c1-1	B

Advanced

a10a1-1	C
a10a1-2	A
a10b1-1	D
a10b2-1	C
a10c1-1	A
a10d1-1	C
a10e1-1	D

11. SAMPLE PAPERS
Foundation

1	A
2	B
3	C
4	C
5	A
6	B
7	B
8	D
9	C
10	B
11	D
12	D
13	B
14	B
15	B
16	A
17	C
18	C
19	C
20	A
21	C
22	D
23	A
24	C
25	D
26	A

Intermediate

1	D
2	B
3	A
4	C
5	D
6	A
7	A
8	C
9	B
10	C
11	C
12	D
13	B
14	D
15	B
16	B
17	A
18	C
19	D
20	B
21	C
22	D
23	B
24	D
25	C
26	B
27	A
28	C
29	D
30	B
31	A
32	B
33	B
34	A
35	C
36	A
37	C
38	A
39	D
40	B
41	C
42	A
43	B
44	D
45	A

Advanced

1	B
2	C
3	C
4	D
5	B
6	D
7	B
8	A
9	D
10	B
11	C
12	A
13	C
14	C
15	C
16	D
17	A
18	D
19	C
20	D
21	C
22	B
23	B
24	A
25	A
26	B
27	B
28	C
29	A
30	C
31	C
32	A
33	A
34	C
35	A
36	D
37	B
38	C
39	B
40	A
41	D
42	D
43	C
44	D
45	B
46	B
47	A
48	C
49	C
50	A
51	B
52	B
53	B
54	A
55	B
56	B
57	D
58	B
59	B
60	B
61	C
62	C

13. Reference Section

PHONETIC ALPHABET

Alpha	Juliet	Sierra
Bravo	Kilo	Tango
Charlie	Lima	Uniform
Delta	Mike	Victor
Echo	November	Whiskey
Foxtrot	Oscar	X-ray
Golf	Papa	Yankee
Hotel	Quebec	Zulu
India	Romeo	

ABBREVIATIONS

There are many abbreviations; these are the examinable ones only.

CQ	Calling signal to establish a contact.
DE	From. M3ABC DE 2E1XYZ would be sent by 2E1XYZ.
DX	Long distance. CQ DX calling long distance, eg another continent.
R	Roger - received and understood.
RST	Signal report - Readability, Signal Strength and Tone.
SIG	Signals.
UR	You are.
WX	Weather.

REGIONAL SECONDARY IDENTIFIERS

E	England (Intermediate callsigns only)
D	Isle of Man
I	Northern Ireland
J	Jersey
M	Scotland
U	Guernsey
W	Wales

COMMON COUNTRY PREFIXES

Only the examinable ones are shown here

EI	Eire
F	France
I	Italy
JA	Japan
PA	The Netherlands
VE	Canada
VK	Australia
W	USA
ZL	New Zealand

Q CODES

The meaning given is the generally accepted amateur usage, which may differ slightly from the meaning given in the international Radio Regulations. For example QRM? Means "are you suffering from interference?" and QRM as a reply means "I am suffering from interference".

QRL?	Are you busy?
QRM	Interference – from man made sources.
QRN	Interference – by natural noise or static.
QRP	Low power or reduce power.
QRT	Stop transmitting.
QRZ?	Who is calling me?
QSB	Fading – the strength of the signal is varying.
QSL	Acknowledgement of receipt. (A QSL card is a written confirmation of a contact.)
QSO	A conversation or communication, a contact.
QSY	Change frequency.
QTH	Location.

MORSE CODE

A	·—	Q	——·—	6	—····		
B	—···	R	·—·	7	——···		
C	—·—·	S	···	8	———··		
D	—··	T	—	9	————·		
E	·	U	··—	0	—————		
F	··—·	V	···—				
G	——·	W	·——				
H	····	X	—··—				
I	··	Y	—·——				
J	·———	Z	——··				
K	—·—						
L	·—··	1	·————				
M	——	2	··———				
N	—·	3	···——				
O	———	4	····—				
P	·——·	5	·····				

Not tested, but you may also meet:

—·—·—

which is the start symbol, and:

·—·—·

which is the end symbol. These are often sent at the beginning and end of a session.

UNIT PREFIXES

pico	10^{-12}	1/1,000,000,000,000	0·000,000,000,001
nano	10^{-9}	1/1,000,000,000	0·000,000,001
micro	10^{-6}	1/1,000,000	0·000,001
milli	10^{-3}	1/1,000	0·001
kilo	10^{3}	1,000	
Mega	10^{6}	1,000,000	
Giga	10^{9}	1,000,000,000	

REFERENCE MATERIAL PROVIDED IN THE EXAMINATIONS

The following pages contain extracts from RCF booklets that are supplied to candidates when taking their examination. The extracts included here will enable you to answer some of the questions included in this book. For those taking the Full Licence it is wise to also have on hand a copy of the Terms, Conditions and Limitations document published by Ofcom.

This can be downloaded from the Ofcom website at www.ofcom.org.uk. As with all documentation the information included here may be different to that supplied for your examination. You do not need to memorise any of this information.

REFERENCE MATERIAL PROVIDED IN THE FOUNDATION LICENCE EXAMINATION

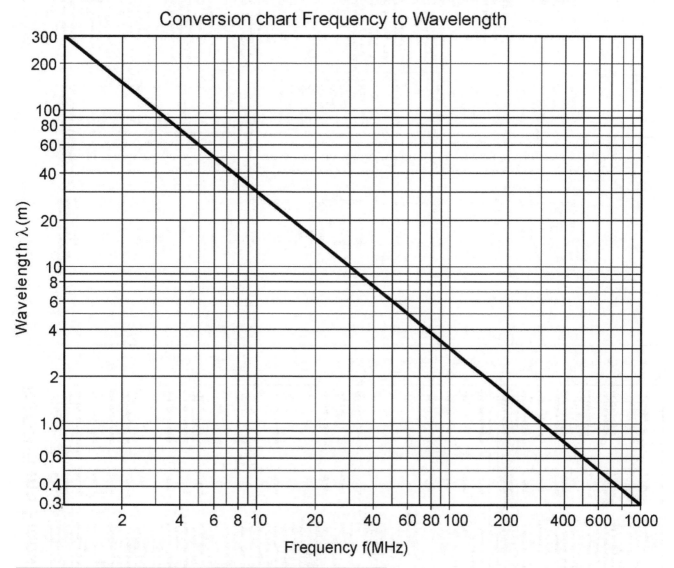

Conversion chart Frequency to Wavelength

Frequency Allocation Table

Frequency	Use
87·5 - 108·0MHz	Broadcasting
108·0 - 117·975MHz	Aeronautical Radionavigation
117·975 - 137·0MHz	Aeronautical Mobile
137·0 - 138·0MHz	Space Operations & Space Research
138·0 - 144·0MHz	Land Mobile
144·0 - 146·0MHz	*Amateur & Amateur Satellite*
146·0 - 149·9MHz	Mobile (except aeronautical mobile)
149·9 - 150·05MHz	Radionavigation-Satellite
150·05 - 152·0MHz	Radio Astronomy
152·0 - 156·0MHz	Land Mobile
156·0 - 158·525MHz	Maritime Mobile
158·525 - 160·6MHz	Land Mobile
160·6 - 160·975MHz	Maritime Mobile

RADIO COMMUNICATIONS FOUNDATION

Foundation Licence Parameters

Frequency Bands (in MHz)	Status of allocations in UK to the Amateur Service	Status of allocations in UK to the Amateur Satellite Service	Maximum Peak Envelope Power level in Watts (and dB relative to 1 Watt)
0.1357-0.1378	Secondary. Available on the basis of non-interference to other services inside or outside the UK.	Not allocated	1W (0 dBW) e.r.p.
1.810-1.830	Primary. Available on the basis of non-interference to other services outside the UK	Not allocated	10W (10 dBW)
1.830-1.850	Primary	Not allocated	10W (10 dBW)
1.850-2.000	Secondary. Available on the basis of non-interference to other services inside or outside the UK.	Not allocated	10W (10 dBW)
3.500-3.800	Primary. Shared with other services	Not allocated	10W (10 dBW)
7.000-7.100	Primary	Primary	10W (10 dBW)
7.100-7.200	Secondary. Available on the basis of non-interference to other services inside or outside the UK.	Not allocated	10W (10 dBW)
10.100-10.150	Secondary	Not allocated	10W (10 dBW)
14.000-14.250	Primary	Primary	10W (10 dBW)
14.250-14.350	Primary	Not allocated	10W (10 dBW)
18.068-18.168	Primary	Primary	10W (10 dBW)
21.000-21.450	Primary	Primary	10W (10 dBW)
24.890-24.990	Primary	Primary	10W (10 dBW)
28.000-29.700	Primary	Primary	10W (10 dBW)
50.00-51.00	Primary. Available on the basis of non-interference to other services outside the UK	Not allocated	10W (10 dBW)
51.00-52.00	Secondary. Available on the basis of non-interference to other services inside the UK	Not allocated	10W (10 dBW)
70.00-70.50	Secondary. Available on the basis of non-interference to other services inside or outside the UK	Not allocated	10W (10 dBW)
144.0-146.0	Primary	Primary	10W (10 dBW)
430.0-431.0	Secondary	Not allocated	10W (10 dBW) e.r.p.
431.0-432.0	Secondary. Not available for use within 100km radius of Charing Cross, London (51°30'30"N, 00°07'24"W)	Not allocated	10W (10 dBW) e.r.p.
432.0-435.0	Secondary	Not allocated	10W (10 dBW)
435.0-438.0	Secondary	Secondary	10W (10 dBW)
438.0-440.0	Secondary	Not allocated	10W (10 dBW)
10000-10125	Secondary	Not allocated	1W (0 dBW)
10225-10450	Secondary	Not allocated	1W (0 dBW)
10450-10475	Secondary	Not allocated	1W (0 dBW)
10475-10500	Not allocated	Secondary	1W (0 dBW)

RSGB Band Plans

Foundation Licence Amateur Radio Band Plans for examination use only

144MHz (2m)	Necessary Bandwidth	UK Usage
144.000-144.110 MHz	500Hz	Telegraphy and data; 144.050 MHz Telegraphy calling
144.110-144.150	500Hz	Telegraphy and data; 144.138 MHz PSK31 centre of activity
144.150-144.180	2700Hz	Telegraphy and data
144.180-144.360	2700Hz	Telegraphy and SSB; 144.150-144.160MHz FAI and Moonbounce (EME) activity SSB; 144.175 MHz Microwave talk-back; 144.200 MHz Random MS SSB calling frequency; 144.250 MHz SSB calling
144.360-144.399	2700Hz	Telegraphy, MGM, SSB; 144.370 MHz MGM calling frequency; GB2RS news broadcast and slow Morse
144.400-144.490		Propagation Beacons only
144.490-144.500		(Guard band)
144.500-144.794	20 kHz	All Modes; 144.500 MHz SSTV calling; 144.525 MHz ATV SSB Talk back; 144.600 MHz RTTY calling; 144.625-144.675 MHz Can be used by RAYNET; 144.700 MHz RTTY working (FSK); 144.750 MHz ATV Talk back; 144.775-144.794 MHz Can be used by RAYNET
144.794-144.990	12 kHz	MGM Packet radio; 144.800-144.9875 MHz Digital modes (including unattended); 144.8250 MHz Internet voice gateway; 144.8375 MHz Internet voice gateway; 144.8500 MHz AX25 BBS user access; 144.9750 MHz High speed 25 kHz channel
144.990-145.1935	12 kHz	FM; RV48 RV63 Repeater input exclusive (Note 2)
145.200	12 kHz	FM; Space communications (e.g. I.S.S.) - Earth-Space
145.200-145.5935	12 kHz	FM; V16-V48 FM simplex (Note 3); 145.2125 MHz Internet voice gateway; 145.2375 MHz Internet voice gateway; 145.2500 MHz Used for slow Morse; 145.2875 MHz Internet voice gateway; 145.3000 MHz RTTY local; 145.3375 MHz Internet voice gateway; 145.5000 MHz Mobile calling; 145.5250 MHz Used for GB2RS news broadcast; 145.5500 MHz Used for rally/exhibition talk-in
145.5935-145.7935	12 kHz	FM; RV48 - RV63 Repeater output (Note 2)
145.800	12 kHz	FM; Space communications (e.g. I.S.S.) - Space-Earth
145.806-146.000	12 kHz	All Modes - Satellite exclusive

Note 1.
Meteor scatter operation can take place up to 20kHz higher than the reference frequency.

Note 2.
12.5kHz channels numbered RV48-RV63. RV48 input = 145.000 MHz, output = 145.600 MHz.

Note 3.
12.5kHz simplex channels numbered V16-V48. V16=145.200 MHz.

Note 4.
Emergency Communications Groups utilising this frequency should take steps to avoid interference to ISS operators in non-emergency situations.

Licence Notes: Amateur Service - Primary: Amateur Satellite Service - Primary User.

14MHz (20m)	Necessary Bandwidth	UK Usage
14,000-14,060 kHz	200 Hz	Telegraph - contest preferred; 14,055 kHz QRS (slow telegraphy) Centre of Activity
14,060-14,070	200 Hz	Telegraphy; 14,060 kHz QRP (low power) Centre of Activity
14,070-14,089	500 Hz	Narrow band modes
14,089-14,099	500 Hz	Narrow band modes - automatically controlled datastations (unattended)
14,101-14,112	2.7 kHz	All modes - automatically controlled data stations (unattended)
14,112-14,125	2.7 kHz	All modes (excluding digimodes)
14,125-14,300	2.7 kHz	All modes SSB contest preferred segment; 14,195 +- 5 kHz Priority for DXpeditions; 14,230 kHz Image Centre of Activity; 14,285 kHz QRP Centre of Activity
14,300-14,350	2.7 kHz	All modes; 14,300 kHz Global Emergency Centre of Activity

14,099-14,101 IBP - reserved exclusively for beacons

Important Note: These band plans have been produced for exam use and are designed to be representative only. These band plans should not be used for on-air activity or as a guide to current practice.

Licence Notes: Amateur Service - Primary; Amateur Satellite Service - Primary User. Beacons may be established for DF competitions except within 50 km of TA012869 (Scarborough).

Frequency Bands (in MHz)	Status of allocations in UK to the Amateur Service	Status of allocations in UK to the Amateur Satellite Service	Maximum Peak Envelope Power level in Watts (and dB relative to 1 Watt)
1240-1260	Secondary	Not allocated	50W (17 dBW)
1260-1270	Secondary	Secondary. Earth to space only	50W (17 dBW)
1270-1325	Secondary	Not allocated	50W (17 dBW)
2310-2400	Secondary	Not allocated	50W (17 dBW)
2400-2450	Secondary. Users must accept interference from ISM users.	Secondary. Users must accept interference from ISM users.	50W (17 dBW)
3400-3475	Secondary	Not allocated	50W (17 dBW)
5650-5670	Secondary	Secondary. Earth to space only	50W (17 dBW)
5670-5680	Secondary	Not allocated	50W (17 dBW)
5755-5765	Secondary. Users must accept interference from ISM users.	Not allocated	50W (17 dBW)
5820-5830	Secondary. Users must accept interference from ISM users.	Not allocated	50W (17 dBW)
5830-5850	Secondary. Users must accept interference from ISM users.	Secondary. Users must accept interference from ISM users. Space to Earth only.	50W (17 dBW)
10000-10125	Secondary	Not allocated	50W (17 dBW)
10225-10450	Secondary	Not allocated	50W (17 dBW)
10450-10475	Secondary	Secondary	50W (17 dBW)
10475-10500	Not allocated	Secondary	50W (17 dBW)
24000-24050	Primary. Users must accept interference from ISM users	Primary. Users must accept interference from ISM users	50W (17 dBW)
24050-24150	Secondary. May only be used with the written consent of Ofcom. Users must accept interference from ISM users	Not allocated	50W (17 dBW)
24150-24250	Secondary	Not allocated	50W (17 dBW)
47000-47200	Primary	Primary	50W (17 dBW)
75500-75875	Secondary	Secondary	50W (17 dBW)
75875-76000	Primary	Primary	50W (17 dBW)
76000-77500	Secondary	Secondary	50W (17 dBW)
77500-78000	Primary	Primary	50W (17 dBW)
78000-79000	Secondary	Secondary	50W (17 dBW)
79000-81000	Secondary	Secondary	50W (17 dBW)
122250-123000	Secondary	Not allocated	50W (17 dBW)
134000-136000	Primary	Primary	50W (17 dBW)
136000-141000	Secondary	Secondary	50W (17 dBW)
241000-248000	Secondary	Secondary	50W (17 dBW)
248000-250000	Primary	Primary	50W (17 dBW)

For examination use only

Intermediate Licence Parameters

Frequency Bands (in MHz)	Status of allocations in UK to the Amateur Service	Status of allocations in UK to the Amateur Satellite Service	Maximum Peak Envelope Power level in Watts (and dB relative to 1 Watt)
0.1357-0.1378	Secondary. Available on the basis of non-interference to other services inside or outside the UK.	Not allocated	1W (0 dBW) e.r.p.
1.810-1.830	Primary. Available on the basis of non-interference to other services outside the UK	Not allocated	50W (17 dBW)
1.830-1.850	Primary	Not allocated	50W (17 dBW)
1.850-2.000	Secondary. Available on the basis of non-interference to other services inside or outside the UK	Not allocated	32W (15 dBW)
3.500-3.800	Primary. Shared with other services	Not allocated	50W (17 dBW)
7.000-7.100	Primary	Primary	50W (17 dBW)
7.100-7.200	Secondary. Available on the basis of non-interference to other services inside or outside the UK	Not allocated	50W (17 dBW)
10.100-10.150	Secondary	Not allocated	50W (17 dBW)
14.000-14.250	Primary	Primary	50W (17 dBW)
14.250-14.350	Primary	Not allocated	50W (17 dBW)
18.068-18.168	Primary	Primary	50W (17 dBW)
21.000-21.450	Primary	Primary	50W (17 dBW)
24.890-24.990	Primary	Primary	50W (17 dBW)
28.000-29.700	Primary	Primary	50W (17 dBW)
50.00-51.00	Primary. Available on the basis of non-interference to other services outside the UK	Not allocated	50W (17 dBW)
51.00-52.00	Secondary. Available on the basis of non-interference to other services inside or outside the UK	Not allocated	50W (17 dBW)
70.00-70.50	Secondary. Available on the basis of non-interference to other services inside or outside the UK	Not allocated	50W (17 dBW)
144.0-146.0	Primary	Primary	50W (17 dBW)
430.0-431.0	Secondary	Not allocated	40W (16 dBW) e.r.p.
431.0-432.0	Secondary. Not available for use within 100km radius of Charing Cross, London (51°30'30"N, 00°07'24"W)	Not allocated	40W (16 dBW) e.r.p.
432.0-435.0	Secondary	Not allocated	50W (17 dBW)
435.0-438.0	Secondary	Secondary	50W (17 dBW)
438.0-440.0	Secondary	Not allocated	50W (17 dBW)

Ofcom Publication for Advanced Licence Examination use only

Schedule 1

Where this Licence is either a Full Licence, a Full (Club) Licence, a Full (Reciprocal) Licence, a Full (Temporary Reciprocal) Licence or a Full (Club) Licence, the Licensee shall only be permitted to operate the Radio Equipment using the frequency bands and power levels set out in Table C of this Schedule 1.

Table C

Full Licence Parameters

Frequency Bands (in MHz)	Status of allocations in UK to the Amateur Service	Status of allocations in UK to the Amateur Satellite Service	Maximum Peak Envelope Power level in Watts (and dB relative to 1 Watt)
0.1357-0.1378	Secondary. Available on the basis of non-interference to other services inside or outside the UK.	Not allocated	1W (0 dBW) e.r.p.
1.810-1.830	Primary. Available on the basis of non-interference to other services outside the UK	Not allocated	400W (26 dBW)
1.830-1.850	Primary	Not allocated	400W (26 dBW)
1.850-2.000	Secondary. Available on the basis of non-interference to other services inside or outside the UK	Not allocated	32W (15 dBW)
3.500-3.800	Primary. Shared with other services	Not allocated	400W (26 dBW)
7.000-7.100	Primary	Primary	400W (26 dBW)
7.100-7.200	Secondary. Available on the basis of non-interference to other services inside or outside the UK	Not allocated	400W (26 dBW)
10.100-10.150	Secondary	Not allocated	400W (26 dBW)
14.000-14.250	Primary	Primary	400W (26 dBW)
14.250-14.350	Primary	Not allocated	400W (26 dBW)
18.068-18.168	Primary	Primary	400W (26 dBW)
21.000-21.450	Primary	Primary	400W (26 dBW)
24.890-24.990	Primary	Primary	400W (26 dBW)
28.000-29.700	Primary	Primary	400W (26 dBW)
50.00-51.00	Primary. Available on the basis of non-interference to other services outside the UK	Not allocated	400W (26 dBW)
51.00-52.00	Secondary. Available on the basis of non-interference to other services inside or outside the UK	Not allocated	100W (20 dBW)
70.00-70.50	Secondary. Available on the basis of non-interference to other services inside or outside the UK	Not allocated	160W (22 dBW)
144.0-146.0	Primary	Primary	400W (26 dBW)
430.0-431.0	Secondary	Not allocated	40W (16 dBW) e.r.p.
431.0-432.0	Secondary. Not available for use, within 100km radius of Charing Cross, London (51°30'30"N, 00°07'24"W)	Not allocated	40W (16 dBW) e.r.p.
432.0-435.0	Secondary	Not allocated	400W (26 dBW)
435.0-438.0	Secondary	Secondary	400W (26 dBW)
438.0-440.0	Secondary	Not allocated	400W (26 dBW)
1240-1260	Secondary	Not allocated	400W (26 dBW)
1260-1270	Secondary	Secondary. Earth to space only	400W (26 dBW)
1270-1325	Secondary	Not allocated	400W (26 dBW)

... continued

Ofcom Publication for Advanced Licence Examination use only

Full Licence Parameters (continued)

Frequency Bands (in MHz)	Status of allocations in UK to the Amateur Service	Status of allocations in UK to the Amateur Satellite Service	Maximum Peak Envelope Power level in Watts (and dB relative to 1 Watt)
2310-2400	Secondary	Not allocated	400W (26 dBW)
2400-2450	Secondary. Users must accept interference from ISM users.	Secondary. Users must accept interference from ISM users.	400W (26 dBW)
3400-3475	Not allocated	Not allocated	400W (26 dBW)
5650-5670	Secondary	Secondary. Earth to space only	400W (26 dBW)
5670-5680	Secondary	Not allocated	400W (26 dBW)
5755-5765	Secondary. Users must accept interference from ISM users	Not allocated	400W (26 dBW)
5820-5830	Secondary. Users must accept interference from ISM users	Not allocated	400W (26 dBW)
5830-5850	Secondary. Users must accept interference from ISM users	Secondary. Users must accept interference from ISM users. Space to Earth only.	400W (26 dBW)
10000-10125	Secondary	Not allocated	400W (26 dBW)
10225-10450	Secondary	Not allocated	400W (26 dBW)
10450-10475	Secondary	Secondary	400W (26 dBW)
10475-10500	Not allocated	Secondary	400W (26 dBW)
24000-24050	Primary. Users must accept interference from ISM users	Primary. Users must accept interference from ISM users	400W (26 dBW)
24050-24150	Secondary. May only be used with the written consent of Ofcom. Users must accept interference from ISM users	Not allocated	400W (26 dBW)
24150-24250	Secondary	Not allocated	400W (26 dBW)
47000-47200	Primary	Primary	400W (26 dBW)
75500-75875	Secondary	Secondary	400W (26 dBW)
75875-76000	Primary	Primary	400W (26 dBW)
76000-77500	Secondary	Secondary	400W (26 dBW)
77500-78000	Primary	Primary	400W (26 dBW)
78000-79000	Secondary	Secondary	400W (26 dBW)
79000-81000	Secondary	Secondary	400W (26 dBW)
122250-123000	Secondary	Not allocated	400W (26 dBW)
134000-136000	Primary	Primary	400W (26 dBW)
136000-141000	Secondary	Secondary	400W (26 dBW)
241000-248000	Secondary	Secondary	400W (26 dBW)
248000-250000	Primary	Primary	400W (26 dBW)

Notes to Schedule 1

(a) dBW is the power level in dB relative to one Watt.

(b) Peak envelope power is the average power supplied to the antenna by a transmitter during one radio frequency cycle at the crest of the modulation envelope taken under normal operating conditions.

(c) Effective radiated power (e.r.p.) (in a given direction) is the product of the power supplied to the antenna and its gain relative to a half-wave dipole in a given direction.

(d) ISM is an abbreviation for industrial, scientific and medical applications.

(e) In all frequency bands, high intensities of radio frequency radiation may be harmful and safety precautions should be taken. Advice concerning safe levels of exposure to radio frequency radiation is provided by the Health Protection Agency.

RSGB Band Plans (effective from 1st December 2006)

The following bandplans are largely based on that agreed at the 2005 IARU Region 1 Conference with some local differences on frequencies above 430 MHz.

144MHz (2m)	Necessary Bandwidth	UK Usage
144.000-144.110MHz	500Hz	**Telegraphy** 144.000-144.035MHz Moonbounce (EME) exclusive 144.050MHz Telegraphy calling 144.100MHz Random MS telegraphy calling (Note 1)
144.110-144.150	500Hz	144.138MHz PSK31 centre of activity 144.120-144.150MHz Moonbounce (EME) MGM (JT65)
144.150-144.180	2.7kHz	144.150-144.160MHz FAI and Moonbounce (EME) activity SSB **Telegraphy and SSB**
144.180-144.360	2.7kHz	144.175MHz Microwave talk-back 144.195-144.205MHz Random MS SSB 144.200MHz Random MS SSB calling frequency 144.250MHz GB2RS news broadcast and slow Morse 144.260MHz Can be used by RAYNET (SSB) 144.300MHz SSB calling
144.360-144.399	2.7kHz	**Telegraphy, MGM, SSB** 144.370MHz MGM calling frequency
144.400-144.490		**Propagation Beacons only** (Guard band)
144.500-144.794	20kHz	**All Modes** 144.500MHz SSTV calling 144.525MHz ATV SSB Talk-back 144.600MHz RTTY calling 144.600MHz RTTY working (FSK) 144.625-144.675MHz Can be used by RAYNET 144.700MHz FAX calling 144.750MHz ATV Talk-back
144.794-144.990	12kHz	144.775-144.794MHz Can be used by RAYNET **MGM Packet radio** 144.800-144.9875MHz Digital modes (inc. unattended) 144.8000MHz Unconnected nets - APRS, UiView etc 144.8250MHz Internet voice gateway 144.8375MHz Internet voice gateway 144.8500MHz AX25 BBS user access 144.8625MHz Available for nodes and BBSs on application 144.8750MHz AX25 TCP/IP user access 144.8875MHz AX25 - priority for DX Cluster access 144.9000MHz AX25 DX Cluster access 144.9250MHz TCP/IP user access 144.9500MHz AX25 BBS user access 144.9750MHz High speed 25 kHz channel
144.990-145.1935	12kHz	**FM** RV48-RV63 Repeater input exclusive (Note 2)
145.200	12kHz	**FM** Space communications (e.g. I.S.S.) - Earth-to-Space 145.2000MHz (Note 4). Can be used by RAYNET
145.200-145.5935	12kHz	**FM** V16-V48 FM simplex (Note 3) 145.2125MHz Internet voice gateway 145.2250MHz Can be used by RAYNET 145.2375MHz Internet voice gateway

144MHz (2m)	Necessary Bandwidth	UK Usage
145.5935-145.7935	12kHz	145.2500MHz Used for slow Morse transmissions 145.2875MHz Internet voice gateway 145.3000MHz RTTY local 145.3375MHz Internet voice gateway 145.5000MHz Mobile calling 145.5250MHz Used for GB2RS news broadcast 145.5500MHz Used for rally/exhibition talk-in
145.800	12kHz	**FM** RV48 - RV63 Repeater output (Note 2)
145.806-146.000	12kHz	**FM** Space communications (e.g. I.S.S.) - Space-Earth **All Modes - Satellite exclusive**

Note 1. Meteor scatter operation can take place up to 26kHz higher than the reference frequency.
Note 2. 12.5kHz channels numbered RV48-RV63. RV48 input = 145.000MHz, output=145.600MHz.
Note 3. 12.5kHz simplex channels numbered V16-V46. V16=145.200MHz.
Note 4. Emergency Communications Groups utilising this frequency should take steps to avoid interference to ISS operations in non-emergency situations.

LICENCE NOTES: Amateur Service & Amateur Satellite Service: **Primary User**
Beacons may be established for DF competions except within 50km of TA012869 (Scarborough).

Ofcom Publication for Advanced Licence Examination use only

Schedule 2
Additional restrictions which apply to the Unattended Operation of Beacons

Frequencies	Full Licence, Full (Reciprocal) Licence, Full (Temporary Reciprocal) Licence, Full (Club) Licence	Intermediate Licence	Foundation Licence
1 960 MHz	(1)	(1)	Not allocated
3.510 MHz -3.543 MHz	(1)	Not allocated	Not allocated
3.553 MHz - 3.600 MHz	(1)	Not allocated	Not allocated
28.000 MHz - 28.100 MHz	Not within 50 km of NGR SK 985640 (1)	Not allocated	Not allocated
28.100 MHz - 28.500 MHz	Not within 50 km of NGR SK 985640 (1)	Not within 50 km of NGR SK 985640 (1)	Not allocated
28.500 MHz – 29.700 MHz	Not within 50 km of NGR SK 985640 (1)	Not allocated	Not allocated
70.000 MHz – 70.500 MHz	Not within 50 km of NGR TA 012869 (1)(2)	Not allocated	Not allocated
144.000 MHz - 146.000 MHz	Not within 50 km of NGR TA 012869 (1)(2)	Not allocated	Not allocated
1298 – 1299 MHz	Not in N. Ireland and not within 50 km of NGR SS 206127 and NGR SE 202577	Not in N. Ireland and not within 50 km of NGR SS 206127 and NGR SE 202577	Not allocated
2310.0000 MHz - 2310.4125 MHz	Not within 50 km of NGR SS 206127 and NGR SE 202577	Not allocated	Not allocated
2310.4125 MHz - 2355.0000 MHz		Not allocated	Not allocated
2355 MHz - 2365 MHz	Not within 50 km of NGR SS 206127 and NGR SE 202577	Not allocated	Not allocated
2365 MHz - 2392 MHz	Not within 50 km of NGR SS 206127 and NGR SE 202577	Not allocated	Not allocated
2392 MHz - 2450 MHz	Not within 50 km of NGR SS 206127 and NGR SE 202577	Not allocated	Not allocated
3400 MHz - 3420 MHz	Not within 50 km of NGR SO 916223, NGR SS 206127 and NGR SE 202577	Not allocated	Not allocated
3420 MHz - 3430 MHz	Not within 50 km of NGR SO 916223, NGR SS 206127 and NGR SE 202577	Not allocated	Not allocated
3430 MHz - 3450 MHz	Not within 50 km of NGR SO 916223, NGR SS 206127 and NGR SE 202577	Not allocated	Not allocated
3450 MHz - 3455 MHz	Not within 50 km of NGR SO 916223, NGR SS 206127 and NGR SE 202577	Not allocated	Not allocated
3455 MHz - 3475 MHz	Not within 50 km of NGR SS 206127 and NGR SE 202577	Not allocated	Not allocated
5650 MHz - 5670 MHz	Not within 50 km of NGR SS 206127 and NGR SE 202577	Not allocated	Not allocated
5670 MHz - 5680 MHz	Not within 50 km of NGR SS 206127 and NGR SE 202577	Not allocated	Not allocated
5755 MHz - 5765 MHz		Not allocated	Not allocated
5820 MHz - 5850 MHz		Not allocated	Not allocated
10000 MHz – 10125 MHz	Not within 50 km of NGR SO 916223, SS 206127, NGR SK 985640 and NGR SE 202577	Not within 50 km of NGR SS 206127, NGR SK 985640 or NGR SE 202577	Not allocated
10400 MHz – 10475 MHz	Not within 50 km of NGR SK 985640 and NGR SE 202577	Not allocated	Not allocated
24000 MHz – 24050 MHz	Not within 50 km of NGR SK 985640 and NGR SE 202577	Not allocated	Not allocated
47000 MHz – 47200 MHz	Not within 50 km of NGR SK 985640 and NGR SE 202577	Not allocated	Not allocated

Notes to additional restrictions which apply to the unattended operation of beacons

(1) May only be used for the purpose of direction finding competitions. The Beacon must transmit the Callsign of the Licensee in accordance with Clause 13 of this Licence and it must be possible to switch the Beacon off within two hours of a demand to close down by a person authorised by Ofcom.

(2) It is permissible to transmit positional information using automatic position reporting software on a spot frequency of 144.800 MHz at any one temporary location not within 50 km of NGR TA 012869. The maximum permitted period of unattended operation is 30 minutes.

Notes to schedule 2

(a) The Unattended Operation of Beacons is only permitted within the frequency bands:

Which are listed in the first column of Schedule 2; or

which are above 75500 MHz and are listed in the first column of Schedule 1 providing that such operation is not within 50 km of NGR SK 985640 and NGR SE 202577.

(b) Beacons may operate with a maximum power level of 25 W e.r.p. pep.

14MHz (20m)	Necessary Bandwidth	UK Usage
14,000-14,060kHz	200Hz	**Telegraphy - contest preferred** 14,055kHz QRS (slow telegraphy Centre of Activity
14,060-14,070	200Hz	**Telegraphy** 14,060kHz QRP (low power) Centre of Activity
14,070-14,089	500Hz	**Narrow band modes**
14,089-14,099	500Hz	**Narrow band modes** - automatically controlled data stations (unattended)
14,099-14,101		**IBP - reserved exclusively for beacons**
14,101-14,112	2.7kHz	**All modes** - automatically controlled data stations (unattended)
14,112-14,125	2.7kHz	**All modes (excluding digimodes)**
14,125-14,300	2.7kHz	**All modes** - SSB contest preferred segment 14,195+/-5kHz Priority for DXpeditions 14,230kHz Image Centre of Activity 14,285kHz QRP Centre of Activity
14,300-14,350	2.7kHz	**All modes** 14,300kHz Global Emergency Centre of Activity

LICENCE NOTES:

Amateur Service - **Primary User.**
14,000-14,250kHz Amateur Satellite Service - **Primary User.**

Notes to the Bandplans

ITU-R Recommendation SM.328 (extract)

Necessary bandwidth: For a given class of emission, the width of the frequency band which is just sufficient to ensure the transmission of information at the rate and with the quality required under specified conditions.

The use of Amplitude Modulation (AM) is acceptable in the all modes segments but users are asked to consider adjacent channel activity when selecting operating frequencies.

Foundation and Intermediate Licence holders are advised to check their licences for the permitted power limits and conditions applicable to their class of licence.

For Advanced Licence Examination use only

Formula sheet

This formula sheet may be used to answer any question.

$R_T = R_1 + R_2 + R_3$	$\dfrac{1}{R_T} = \dfrac{1}{R_1} + \dfrac{1}{R_2} + \dfrac{1}{R_3}$	$V = IR$
$V_{out} = V_{in}\dfrac{R_2}{R_1+R_2}$	$P = VI = \dfrac{V^2}{R} = I^2R$	$V_{rms} = \dfrac{V_{peak}}{\sqrt{2}}$
$Z = \sqrt{R^2 + X^2}$	$V_T = \sqrt{V_R^2 + V_C^2}$ (or V_L^2)	$X_C = \dfrac{1}{2\pi fC}$
$L_T = L_1 + L_2 + L_3$	$\dfrac{1}{L_T} = \dfrac{1}{L_1} + \dfrac{1}{L_2}$	$X_L = 2\pi fL$
$\dfrac{1}{C_T} = \dfrac{1}{C_1} + \dfrac{1}{C_2} + \dfrac{1}{C_3}$	$C_T = C_1 + C_2 + C_3$	$C = \dfrac{kA}{d}$ where $k = \varepsilon_0 \varepsilon_r$
$f = \dfrac{1}{2\pi\sqrt{LC}}$	$T = \dfrac{1}{f}$	$\tau = CR$
$Q = \dfrac{2\pi fL}{R}$ or $\dfrac{1}{2\pi fCR}$	$Q = \dfrac{f_C}{f_U - F_L} = \dfrac{\text{centre frequency}}{\text{bandwidth}}$	$R_D = \dfrac{L}{CR}$
$Q = 2\pi fCR_D$		
$V_S = V_P\dfrac{N_S}{N_P}$	$I_P = I_S\dfrac{N_S}{N_P}$	$Z_P = Z_S\left(\dfrac{N_P}{N_S}\right)^2$
$I_C = \beta I_B$	$f_{step} = \dfrac{f_{crystal}}{A}$	$F_{out} = f_{crystal}\dfrac{N}{A}$
$c = 3\times10^8$ m/s	$\text{Gain (loss)} = 10\,Log_{10}\dfrac{\text{power out}}{\text{power in}}$ dB	$SWR = \dfrac{V_{max}}{V_{min}} = \dfrac{V_f + V_r}{V_f - V_r}$
$v = f\lambda$	$\text{Gain (loss)} = 20\,Log_{10}\dfrac{\text{voltage out}}{\text{voltage in}}$ dB	$Z_0^2 = Z_{in}\times Z_{out}$
$E = \dfrac{7\sqrt{erp}}{d}$	$\text{Return Loss} = 10\,Log_{10}\dfrac{\text{Reflected power}}{\text{Incident power}}$	$bw = 2(\Delta F_{max} + \Delta f)$
$erp = $ power $\times$ gain (linear)	$\text{Gain} = 10\,Log_{10}\dfrac{\text{power from Yagi}}{\text{power from dipole}}$ dBd